2004 POET

ONCE UPON A RHYME

IMAGINATION FOR A NEW GENERATION

Scottish Regions
Edited by Steve Twelvetree

 Young**Writers**

First published in Great Britain in 2005 by:
Young Writers
Remus House
Coltsfoot Drive
Peterborough
PE2 9JX
Telephone: 01733 890066
Website: www.youngwriters.co.uk

SB ISBN 1 84460 649 X

Foreword

Young Writers was established in 1991 and has been passionately devoted to the promotion of reading and writing in children and young adults ever since. The quest continues today. Young Writers remains as committed to engendering the fostering of burgeoning poetic and literary talent as ever.

This year's Young Writers competition has proven as vibrant and dynamic as ever and we are delighted to present a showcase of the best poetry from across the UK. Each poem has been carefully selected from a wealth of *Once Upon A Rhyme* entries before ultimately being published in this, our twelfth primary school poetry series.

Once again, we have been supremely impressed by the overall high quality of the entries we have received. The imagination, energy and creativity which has gone into each young writer's entry made choosing the best poems a challenging and often difficult but ultimately hugely rewarding task - the general high standard of the work submitted amply vindicating this opportunity to bring their poetry to a larger appreciative audience.

We sincerely hope you are pleased with our final selection and that you will enjoy *Once Upon A Rhyme Scottish Regions* for many years to come.

Contents

Auchtertool Primary School, Auchtertool

Andrew Kerr (8)	15
Holly Gallagher (9)	16
Michael Hutchison (10)	16
Thomas Hutchison (8)	16
Heather Mary Macduff (9)	17
Zara Lawrence (9)	17
Emma Laing (8)	18
Scott Fernie (9)	18
Phillip Duckett (7)	19
Kristoffer Patrick (10)	19
Rebecca Wilson (9)	19
Deema Chehade (8)	20
Emma Scott	20
Ayesha Siddique (11)	21
Fiona Rennie (10)	21
Calum Adams (8)	22
Mani Siddique (10)	22

Colinsburgh Primary School, Fife

Kayleigh Wood (7)	22
Sharece Burnett (10)	23
Declan Fielmar (9)	24
Marc Robertson (9)	25
Kayleigh Dewar (8)	25
Niall Hutchison (11)	26
Lewis Rabjohns (9)	27
Robbie Provan (10)	28
Laura MacDonald (10)	29
Graeme Peebles (11)	30
Sandy Dunsire (8)	31
Connor Hutchison (7)	31
Nicole Simpson (9)	32
Connor Wood (9)	33
Bronwen Parker (7)	33
Andrew Gardner (10)	34
Craig Blyth (9)	35
Charlotte Haigh (10)	36
Mark Haigh (8)	37
Danielle Leitch (8)	37
Margaret McCall (8)	38

Craigrothie Primary School, Fife

Jane Bullivant (11)	38
Caitlin Sinclair (8)	39
John Bullivant (9)	39
Ryan Kaempfe (8)	39
Kyle Andrew Small (9)	40
Sean Alexander Cowan (11)	40
Kirsty MacKay (11)	41
Brogan Sinclair (9)	41
Fraser Wilson (9)	42
Leah Reid (8)	42
Ewan Anderson (8)	43
Jack Wilson (9)	43
Eve Sinclair (8)	43
Catriona MacKay (11)	44
Daniel Henderson (10)	44
Caitlin Stewart (8)	44

David Livingstone Memorial Primary School, Blantyre

David Andrews (10)	45
Louise Parsons (9)	45
Laura Vance (10)	46
Nadine Shaban Salim (9)	46
Blair Armstrong (10)	47
William Hughes (10)	47

Garscadden Primary School, Glasgow

Rakhsana Ishaq (9)	48
Kurtis Roberts (10)	48
Courtney O'Neill (10)	49
Alasdair McKechnie (10)	49
Hannah Jenkins (9)	50
Charlotte Gillian Ross (10)	50
Leeanne Robertson (9)	50
Beeza Ahmed (10)	51
Roísín Vagg (9)	51
Hollie Boyd (9)	51
Rachel Louise Walker (10)	52
Somaya Naas (11)	52
Andrew Robertson (11)	52
Eden Thomson (10)	53

Linzi Hamilton (10)	53
Kyle McGeoch (10)	53
Gillian Deans (10)	54
Billy Munro (11)	54
Megan Lee (10)	55
Jodie Hamilton (10)	55
Samantha MacMillan (11)	55
Emma Furie (10)	56
Faisal Byansi (10)	56
Laura Keen (10)	56
Andrew Peddie (11)	57
Darren Campbell (11)	57
Kulbir Gabba	57
Craig Morrison (11)	58
Sophie Ellis (10)	58
Jaye Berry (11)	58

Garthamlock Primary School, Glasgow

Ann Nicol (9)	59
Jillian Gray (10)	60
Leanne Hendry (11)	61
Dillon McGovaney (11)	62
Ashley Dailly (11)	63
Michelle Reilly (11)	64
Jane Cunningham (11)	65
Danielle Woods (11)	66

Killearn Primary School, Glasgow

David Leonard (8)	66
Niamh Turner (9)	67
Flora Matthews (9)	67
Kirsty Findlay (8)	67
Angus North (9)	68
Alexander Russell (8)	68
Danny Corcoran (8)	68
Calum Norval (8)	68
Louise Bell (9)	69
Jasmine Leung (9)	69
Fraser Glencross (8)	69
Alan Beattie (9)	69
Blair Cooper (8)	70

Kirstie Buchanan (9)　　　　　　　　70
Kirsten Tempest (8)　　　　　　　　70
Amy McNeill (9)　　　　　　　　　71
Katie Hughes (9)　　　　　　　　71
Robert Cowden (8)　　　　　　　　71

McGill Primary, Bonnyholm Campus, Glasgow

Amanda Jane McEwing (10)　　　　72
Gemma Reilly (10)　　　　　　　72
Gavin Docherty (10)　　　　　　72
Sean McKinney (11)　　　　　　73
Yousif Al-Ani (10)　　　　　　73
Stuart Beveridge (10)　　　　　73
Rachael Donaghy (11)　　　　　74
Jordan Kilday (11)　　　　　　74
Rebecca Lees (9)　　　　　　74
Lisa McLauchlan (11)　　　　　75
Amy McLachlan (9)　　　　　　75
Siobhan Seils (10)　　　　　　75

Mossneuk Primary School, East Kilbride

Angela Teape (8)　　　　　　　76
Heather McColl　　　　　　　　76
Ryan Brown (7)　　　　　　　76
Jonathan Aitken (8)　　　　　　77
Michael Waddell (8)　　　　　77
Heather Neil (8)　　　　　　　77
Ewan Gibson (8)　　　　　　78
Connor McBrearty (8)　　　　　78
Katie MacMillan (8)　　　　　78
Holly Sheen (8)　　　　　　　79
Ross McKechnie　　　　　　　79
Razak Hunter (8)　　　　　　79

Mount Florida Primary School, Glasgow

Calum Ewing-Hepburn (9)　　　　80
Jenna Cook (9)　　　　　　　80
Ryan Melville (9)　　　　　　81
Rachel Murray (10)　　　　　　81
Maxine Cassidy (10)　　　　　81
Shelley Goldie (10)　　　　　82

Natalie Kenyon-Alonso (9)	82
Robert John Whelan (9)	83
Nicola Kennedy (10)	83
Karen Laycock (9)	83
Sharon Singh (9)	84
Jordan Fong (10)	84
Emma Lavery (10)	84
Rebecca McGeary (9)	85
Alix Fleming (9)	85
Daniel McCalman (10)	85
Lauren Pettigrew (10)	86
Luke Horne (9)	86
Olivia Pettigrew (9)	87
Helen Anderson (10)	87
Kitty Hodgman (10)	88
Scott Gallacher (10)	88
Tahir Anwar (10)	88

Notre Dame Primary School, Glasgow

Caroline Gilday (10)	89
Sean Morgan (10)	90
Alessandro Marini (10)	90
Ruaridh Frize (11)	91
Ché Julienne-Chalmers (11)	91
Kumba Dauda (11)	92
Lauren Reilly (10)	92
Amy Beer (11)	93
Tor Brooke (11)	94
Holly Leonard (11)	95
Saahirah Mohammed (10)	95
Natalie Bertagna (10)	96
Taylor Kim (10)	96
Ayesha Mohammed (10)	97
Naveen Qureshi (10)	98
Jemma McDermott (10)	98
Nyala Arshad (10)	99
Georgina Dunne (9)	99
Jonathan Sheridan (11)	99
Ciára Robinson (10)	100
Nisha Mohammed (10)	100
Eva Bloice (10)	100

Hannah Oliver (9)   101
Callia Soave (10)   102
Kordian Gil (10)   103
Martin Scullion (10)   103
Emily Burns (10)   103
Rosie Birchard (10)   104
Simone Walsh (10)   104
Philip Law (10)   105
Emily Crockett (9)   105
Nicole Rae (10)   105
Kerry O'Donnell (10)   106
Christopher Bland (10)   106
Eva Grant (9)   106
Gennaro Capaldi (10)   107

Pathhead Primary School, Kirkcaldy
Jordanne McMillan (10)   107
Robin Hagley (10)   107
Kirsty Ray (10)   108
Danielle Johnston (10)   108
Demi Roza (10)   108
Hazel Robb (10)   109
Brandon Proctor (9)   109
Samantha Tait (9)   109
Natalie Minick (9)   110

Rephad Primary School, Stranraer
Dean McRobert (10)   110
James McHarrie (11)   110
Blair Forsyth (11)   111
Stuart Monteith (11)   111
Andy Lock (11)   112
Ian Cowan (11)   112
Kirsty Park (10)   112
Angus Michael Cochrane (11)   113
Steven Leek (11)   113
Erica McGeoch (11)   114
Ross Hughes (11)   114
Amy Hastings (11)   115
Alex Halliday (10)   115
Christopher Batty (11)   115

Darren Stewart (11) 129
Andrew O'Brien 129
Jade Lindsay (11) 130
Emma Gavan (10) 130
Kimberley McElwaine (10) 131

St Joseph's Primary School, Busby
Ursula Welsh (8) 131
Ciara Lawwell (8) 132
Petrena Marshall (9) 132
Hannah Siobhan Cantley (8) 133
Colin Campbell (9) 133
Kathryn Mesarowicz (9) 134
Kathryn Mahon (8) 134
Lucy Caldwell (9) 135
Kelsey Comerford (9) 136
Victoria Caldwell (8) 136
Amanda Devlin (8) 137
Neale Waugh (9) 137
Jack Henry (9) 138
Sean Merrick (8) 139
Connor McKeown (8) 139
Rachel McCallum (9) 140

St Mary's RC Primary School, Stirling
Jerrylee McGowan (9) 140
Nico Burns (10) 141
Ryan Watson (10) 141
Paige Kilbane (10) 142
Corrina Hamilton (9) 142
Nathan Logan (9) 143
Leonie Coyle (9) 143
Amanda McMinn (10) 144
Logen Ludwig (11) 144
Caitlin Robertson (11) 145
Kim Lynch (9) 145
Louise Watson (11) 146
Marc McGowan (11) 146
Stephen Lewis (10) 147

St Michael's Primary School, Moodiesburn

Caitlin Elliot (9)	147
Andrew Cairns (10)	148
Caitlin Fleming (8)	148
Declan Fitzsimmons (11)	149
Lauren McLelland (8)	149
Rachael McPake (11)	150
Derek Marr (9)	150
Aynsley Murphy (11)	151
Michelle Taggarty (11)	151
Eilidh Swinton (8)	152
Aiden Connolly (10)	152
Shannon O'Hara (10)	153
Antonia Dick (7)	153
Kayleigh Fleming (10)	154
Liam Ross (6)	154
Mark Kiernan (11)	155
Erin Pender (11)	155
Melissa Johnson (11)	156
Hannah McInally (7)	156
Jack Berry (10)	157
Paul Slaven (9)	157
Laura Kelly (11)	158
Teigan Jamieson (7)	158
Michael Myers (11)	159
Megan McNicol (6)	159
Michaella Johnson (9)	160
Stewart Hendry (9)	160
Calum McKinnon (8)	161
Dionne Johnson (9)	161
Katie Flaherty (10)	162
Aidan Lochrie (7)	162
Ross Clark (11)	163
Danielle Corrigan (7)	163
Murray Crossan (11)	164
Lauren McLeish (7)	164
Aydan Topping (10)	165
Jamie Quate (8)	165
Paul Brennan (10)	166
Laura Friel (7)	166
Declyn Emslie (11)	167

Ryan Kelly (8)	167
Robert Gracie (10)	168
Declan McKean (7)	168
Shannon Love (11)	169
Jon Devlin (11)	170
Emma Rodgers (10)	170
Michelle McCabe (11)	171
Kirsten MacFarlane (9)	171
Nicola Murray (10)	172
Kate Hardie (9)	173
Victoria Lowe (9)	173
Staci Brady (9)	174
Lisa Marie Mitchell (9)	174
Conor Lochrie (9)	175
Claire Gallagher (8)	175
Alana Dunion (9)	176
Brendan Johnson (7)	176
Rachel Cannon (7)	176
Ashley Welch (8)	177
Joni Moultrie (9)	177
Danielle Cochrane (9)	178
Colette McGarry (9)	178

St Thomas' Primary School, Neilston

Katie MacKenzie (9)	179
Megan McCarron (9)	179
Joe Foy (9)	179
Katelin Wilson (8)	180
Jordan Whiteford (9)	180
Sophie McAvoy (9)	180
Annelouise McCullagh (9)	181
Hannah Moore (8)	181
Sara Howie (8)	181
Kendle Keenan (9)	182
Brogan McFlynn (9)	182
Daniella Di Bona (9)	182
Nicola Finnigan (9)	183
Liam Brady (9)	183
Danielle Higgins (8)	183
Neil Morran (8)	184
Adam Martin (9)	184

Tingwall Primary School, Shetland Islands

The Poems

Happiness

Happiness is the blue, sparkling sky on a hot summer's day,
Happiness is the magical sound of the birds singing in
                                        the old conker tree,
Happiness is the mouth-watering taste of chocolate cake,
Happiness is the delicious smell of scrumptious cake
                                        cooking in the oven,
Happiness feels like a fluffy ball of candyfloss,
Happiness is when school is over for the holidays.

Sheona Callen Smith (8)
Ancrum Primary School, Jedburgh

Happiness

Happiness is red like a rose blossoming on a summer's day,
Happiness is the tinkling sound of a fairy talking,
Happiness tastes like the chocolate melting on my ice cream,
Happiness smells of some sweet berries in the woods,
Happiness feels like I am free,
Happiness is Busted!

Marie Driver (6)
Ancrum Primary School, Jedburgh

Happiness

Happiness is red like a juicy plum,
Happiness is the sound of children singing 'Happy Birthday.'
Happiness is the mouth-watering taste of an apple,
Happiness smells of home-made soup,
Happiness is stroking a soft furry cat,
Happiness is waking up at Christmas.

Jared Birse (6)
Ancrum Primary School, Jedburgh

Happiness

Happiness is the colours of the shiny rainbow,
That makes me feel warm inside,
Happiness is the magical sound of a beautiful
                    robin singing in the old, old oak tree,
Happiness is the delicious taste of crunchy vegetarian bacon,
Happiness is the fresh smell of a beautiful rose that
                         makes me smile my magical smile,
Happiness feels like my mum cuddling me,
Happiness is coming back to school on the first day of term.

Ailsa Davie (8)
Ancrum Primary School, Jedburgh

Happiness

Happiness is the white snow falling on me,
Happiness is the splashing sound of a waterfall,
Happiness is the delicious taste of mini pizza,
Happiness is the smell of a red rose,
Happiness is going on holiday,
Happiness is going to sleep, thinking about Santa Claus.

Robert Horne (6)
Ancrum Primary School, Jedburgh

Happiness

Happiness is the light blue of the sky on a summer's day,
Happiness sounds like a cat purring,
Happiness is the delicious taste of sweetcorn dripping with butter,
Happiness is the fresh small of cream,
Happiness feels like a kitten sitting on my lap,
Happiness is waking up on Christmas Day and getting
                              lots of presents.

Shanna Johnston (7)
Ancrum Primary School, Jedburgh

Happiness

Happiness is the bright orange of the hot blazing sun
That's shining on you and me,
Happiness is the relaxing sound of the sparkling water
Trickling down the sweet little stream,
Happiness is the delicious taste of chocolate melting
                                        on my tongue,
Happiness is the lovely smell of a beautiful blossom
                                tree blowing in the wind.
Happiness feels like a white blanket of snow in the winter,
Happiness is waking up on Christmas Day.

Caitlin Dunbar (8)
Ancrum Primary School, Jedburgh

Happiness

Happiness is the red of a juicy strawberry,
Happiness is the chirping of the birds in the hedge,
Happiness is the taste of a lip-smacking orange,
Happiness smells like a red rose,
Happiness feels like some candyfloss,
Happiness is playing on my bike.

Connor Millar (7)
Ancrum Primary School, Jedburgh

Happiness

Happiness is the deep, dark, blue sea,
Happiness is the sound of the sea splashing against the rocks,
Happiness is the taste of salty sea water,
Happiness is the fresh smell of the breeze,
Happiness feels like my cat sitting on my knee,
Happiness is going on a big holiday.

Grant Paxton (7)
Ancrum Primary School, Jedburgh

Happiness

Happiness is a red, juicy, ripe apple,
Happiness is the scrumptious taste of a cheese toastie
melting in your mouth.
Happiness is the beautiful sound of birds chirping merrily,
Happiness smells like the fresh sky on top of the mountain,
Happiness feels like my dog cuddling me on my legs,
Happiness is going on holiday with my family.

Helen Whillans (7)
Ancrum Primary School, Jedburgh

Happiness

Happiness is the clear blue sky on a sunny day,
Happiness is the beautiful sound of the birds singing on the ark,
Happiness is the scrumptious taste of home-made bread,
Happiness is the lovely smell of fresh chocolate cake,
Happiness feels like a furry dog sitting on your knee,
Happiness is playing in the snow.

Nicholas Arnold (7)
Ancrum Primary School, Jedburgh

Happiness

Happiness is white like a frosty winter morning,
Happiness is the cheerful sound of birds singing,
Happiness is the mouth-watering taste of sugary sweets,
Happiness smells like fresh home-made bread,
Happiness feels like a little furry kitten on my lap,
Happiness is waking up on Christmas Day.

Daire Harvey (8)
Ancrum Primary School, Jedburgh

Happiness

Happiness is the dark, black sky on the dark winter's night,
Happiness is the rumble of thunder in the dark, stormy sky,
Happiness is the scrumptious taste of dark chocolate
                                    cake in my mouth,
Happiness is the smell of sweet chocolate cake,
Happiness feels like a soft dog,
Happiness is playing on my trampoline.

Rory Marshall (8)
Ancrum Primary School, Jedburgh

Happiness

Happiness is dark blue like the sea at night,
Happiness sounds like the rumbling of thunder in the dark sky,
Happiness is the scrumptious taste of pizza,
Happiness smells like fresh air on the mountain top,
Happiness feels like leaves crunching on the ground,
Happiness is when school is over for the summer holidays.

Cameron Munro (8)
Ancrum Primary School, Jedburgh

Happiness

Happiness is the bright green grass in my garden,
Happiness is the great roar of thunder in the black stormy sky,
Happiness is the glorious taste of home-made pizza,
Happiness is the fruity smell of a home-made smoothie,
Happiness feels like my dog licking me,
Happiness is waking up on the first day of the summer holidays
And going out to play.

Scott Samson (8)
Ancrum Primary School, Jedburgh

Happiness

Happiness is the bright blue of the big wide ocean,
Happiness is the sound of the beautiful birds singing in the sky,
Happiness is the delicious taste of a pepperoni pizza,
Happiness is the lovely smell of my tea cooking,
Happiness feels like a fluffy dog,
Happiness is when I wake up on my birthday.

Rory Smith (8)
Ancrum Primary School, Jedburgh

All Sorts Of Weather

The weather is all different things
When the snow falls there are lots of snowballs too!
But when it gets cold and you start to shiver,
Your hands go numb, it's a different story,
Sun is the summer, hot as fire,
Nice to play a frisbee game, in the hot sun,
Rain so boring, so wet,
But don't need to fuss,
Have a water fight instead!

Amy Geddes (10)
Antonine Primary School, Bonnybridge

Animal Poem

I went into the zoo and
Tigers were roaring very loud,
Monkeys were climbing fast,
Turtles were going as slow as they could,
Fish were wiggling their bodies as they swam,
Lions were snoring as they slept,
Pandas were chasing after the zookeeper -
It was a disaster!

Rabia Rashad (10)
Antonine Primary School, Bonnybridge

Number One Mum

Mum's never tired,
Mum never sleeps,
Dad tries the same,
But he's too weak.

Dad's too lazy,
Never Mum,
Amusing,
And lots of fun.

When Dad takes us on holiday,
While we're all riding boats,
She'll be cooking and cleaning,
And she doesn't even smoke.

She's Super Mum,
She's funny,
She's not mean about money,
Even Dad knows that she's the best.

Ewan Anderson (10)
Antonine Primary School, Bonnybridge

The Zombie Walking Down The Street

I was walking down the street
When I met someone weird to meet
And with surprise he had hardly any feet!
It was the zombie walking down the street,
He was skin and bones and swords and blood,
'Hello' he said and I said, 'Who are you?'
He replied, 'I'm the *zombie!*
And my friend's would like to eat you!
Ha, ha, ha, ha, ha!'

Thomas Baird (10)
Antonine Primary School, Bonnybridge

Underwater Life

Fish get caught for our tea
Seaweed green, seaweed I hate
Sand at the bottom
Where fish have died
Dolphins jump over the waves
Divers swim down to the bottom
And are dinner for the sharks,
Have you seen a very big fish?
A whale will eat you in a flash
Have you seen an 8-legged fish?
It is an octopus,
A friend of mine, *not!*
Hear this - a shark can kill so hear this -
A deadly animal is loose around.

Stephanie Dunsmore (10)
Antonine Primary School, Bonnybridge

Summer Sunshine

Playing on the beach, oh what fun,
Playing in the water getting very wet,
Laughing and giggling,
Singing a happy tune,
We stayed till night,
For the fireworks which had a big boom,
After Dad came for us, he said,
'Did you have a good time?'
'Yeah!' We shouted
As we went to bed.

Steven Harris (10)
Antonine Primary School, Bonnybridge

Spooky

I went inside the library
Inside was all spidery.

Magic books flying
An old lady crying.

An old man humming
Cats prancing and running.

Mayhem in the library.

I was walking down the street
The weather was sleet.

Walking up the stairs
While eyes stare.

Jumping in my bed
Voices said

'*Beware* of the monster under the bed!'

Victoria Dunsmore (9)
Antonine Primary School, Bonnybridge

Monster Tower

Monster Tower is like Ardgour moving every hour,
Place to place, staircase to staircase ,
Monsters running,
People humming,
Hissing cats, barking dogs, swampy bogs,
Monster Tower has lots of power,
Mystical magic,
Zooming gadgets,
Black bats scratching cats.

Ryan Gibson (10)
Antonine Primary School, Bonnybridge

Monsta Football

One day I was playing football in the street,
Then I smelt the smell of smelly feet,
I didn't think it was much of a treat,
The next moment I saw a light,
It gave me such a fright.
Then I went and peeked
I swear I could have shrieked,
I saw an alien
He said his name was Yoyo
He asked if I liked footie,
I totally love playing footie,
Then he pulled bombs from his back,
And said 'I hope you do not hack'
Then the bombs went boom . . .
I heard the fans cheering,
Then Yoyo came nearing,
'You are officially in the Monsta Carlo Stadium.'
Then I went on
I got the ball,
I whizzed by a dragon
And tried not to fall,
I now had an open goal
And to shoot I was told
Then I shot
      It was a pot
           Right into
                The top.
This was like a dream,
Then a dragon let off steam
Then in a flash I woke up, it was a dream!

Scott Johnston (10)
Antonine Primary School, Bonnybridge

Flowers, What's The Point?

Flowers are beautiful so to say,
But they need water, soil and day,
Some flowers smell like perfume, some smell nice,
Some smell disgusting like rice,
I hate rice, it stinks!
I think some look nice, some look ugly,
I mean like really yucky!
Some grow here and there,

Some grow everywhere! That's the point in flowers,
To spread themselves across the land,
They're fast to grow,
Faster than Grand Prix stand,
With Michael Schumacher,
Ohh, what's the point in flowers!

Laura Walker (10)
Antonine Primary School, Bonnybridge

Football

Some boys play football kicking it around
Oops it's in the garden shouting all around.

Old rusty football goals hanging by a string
People hitting shots and they're just about collapsing.

The ball goes in the river
New trainers get all wet.

Get all mucky and clothes get grass-stained,
That's how they like to play.

Geeky people do not play,
So we shout and they walk away.

Jack McCue (9)
Antonine Primary School, Bonnybridge

Merry Christmas

M any people dancing and singing,
E lves running around making the toys,
R udolph and his red shining nose,
R eindeer pulling Santa's sleigh,
Y ummy cookies being eaten by Santa.

C rackers bursting at the Christmas dinner,
H ats from crackers being worn all day through,
R elatives popping over to say 'Merry Christmas'
I ce being skated on by lots of children,
S anta going down chimneys and dropping off toys,
T all Christmas trees getting in Santa's way,
M ums and dads getting silly adult presents,
A unts and uncles organising parties,
S anta goes home to sleep for another year.

Elliot McMenemy (9)
Antonine Primary School, Bonnybridge

Bad Weather

B lizzards in the Arctic,
A sia's sun is burning,
D allas in America isn't always hot.

W et and cold in Scotland,
E thiopia is never wet and drizzly,
A ntarctica has too many blizzards,
T hunder and lightning in Wales,
H arrogate isn't the best of places,
E nniskillen has a big castle but it's always raining,
R io, here we have great fun and it's always hot.

Craig O'Neill (9)
Antonine Primary School, Bonnybridge

Thunder

T hunder thrashing up and down,
H unters out in the rain,
U nder the rain it spooks me out,
N othing to do, it's boring inside,
D ull, dull, dull all day,
E ating popcorn, watching TV,
R unning around playing hide-and-seek,

Now it is sunny
Let's go and play outside!

Sarah Stephen (10)
Antonine Primary School, Bonnybridge

Dornay

D ays are never boring at Dornay,
O tters live in the loch in Dornay,
R un and play hide-and-seek, full of happiness,
N ever sad in Dornay, full of happiness,
A fter nights there's lots of fun,
Y ellow sunshine full of fun.

Hannah Murray (10)
Antonine Primary School, Bonnybridge

Snail Trail

A snaily trail is beautiful with its dazzling rainbow colours.
It is very slimy and wobbly.
The strange thing about trails is, you never know if it has
been done by a slug or a snail.
But if you follow it very closely you will see,
Following a snail's trail lets you see where it has been.

Sophie Whiteford (9)
Antonine Primary School, Bonnybridge

Animal Kingdom

Grumpy cats like,
Eating tiny rats.

Wild dogs like,
Chasing little hedgehogs.

Big mice like,
Eating tiny woodlice.

Giant tigers like,
Stepping on teeny spiders.

All the animals of the animal kingdom,
I wish I could be an animal too!

Rebecca Moir (10)
Antonine Primary School, Bonnybridge

Teachers

Teachers, teachers old and nice,
Teachers, teachers they all like mice.

Teachers, teachers crabby and ugly,
Teachers, teachers nice and cuddly.

Teachers, teachers moan all day,
Teachers, teachers get a good pay.

Teachers, teachers smell all day,
Teachers, teachers shout all the way.

Teachers, teachers tall and short,
Teachers, teachers have lots of warts.

Megan Smith (9)
Antonine Primary School, Bonnybridge

Baby Animals

Puppies like to run around,
Bounce all day and dig up the ground.

Kittens like to pounce on mice,
I think their fur is very nice.

Foals like to run in fields,
And have very tasty meals.

Mice like to creep at night,
Also they are very light.

Chloe Peat (9)
Antonine Primary School, Bonnybridge

Harvest

Plant a seed, watch it grow,
That's how they farmed years ago,
Through the summer, through the winter,
All day long,
New machinery, old machinery,
That's how it goes,
We go through the long days
And through the short ones,
Using old and new machinery.

Daniel Wilson (9)
Antonine Primary School, Bonnybridge

At The Seaside

At the seaside I can see,
Huge dolphins dancing in the sea,
Snatching silver fish trying to escape,
Every dolphin dives back into the sea,
Leaving bubbles behind them.

Andrew Kerr (8)
Auchtertool Primary School, Auchtertool

The Storm

I lay in my bed one cold, stormy night,
To listen to the sound of the blasting storm,
It whistled and flashed,
Till it broke my window glass,
It calmed down,
Till a sudden smash,
The lightning had split my favourite tree,
It gave me a fright,
The storm.

Holly Gallagher (9)
Auchtertool Primary School, Auchtertool

A Lonely Giant

The old lonely giant,
Lives up a snowy jaggy mountain,
The world he sees as a microscopic busy toy,
He only eats grizzly bears, his favourite food,
He has no mates,
When he comes down,
The people run away,
He sits there crying.

Michael Hutchison (10)
Auchtertool Primary School, Auchtertool

Army Soldier

Army soldier hiding in the long grass and bushes,
Army soldier waiting to attack for the first time,
Army soldier breathing in the muddy, grassy air,
Army soldier crawling like a lizard,
Army soldier rustling leaves under his boots,
Army soldier firing his gun and shouting.

Thomas Hutchison (8)
Auchtertool Primary School, Auchtertool

Walking Dogs

Four bouncy dogs,
Running across the grass,
I'd better hurry or
I'll be last,
Mum calls out their names,
But they don't come back,
They hide from us
In the bushes and dark,
Rustling noises,
Snuffling of noses,
I blow the whistle loud,
They hurry back,
What fun we have on our walks,
Four bouncy dogs,
Running home fast
Leaving me behind
I'm always last.

Heather Mary Macduff (9)
Auchtertool Primary School, Auchtertool

My Pet Monster

I have a pet monster,
Under my bed,
He is my best friend,
He comes out at night,
To give me a fright,
We play spooky games,
He is friendly and won't hurt me,
We dance and sing to music,
It's all fun and games until daylight,
At dawn he has to go back under
So goodbye to my pet monster.

Zara Lawrence (9)
Auchtertool Primary School, Auchtertool

An Old, Old Haunted House

Towards the old mansion I walked,
But when I got there, the door was locked,
Scary sounds filled the air,
Staring eyes are everywhere,
Owls, mice, spiders and bats,
Witches on broomsticks with their cats,
I saw the key upon the stair,
I tried the lock with great care,
I opened the door,
And stepped on the floor,
It made my knees weak,
When the boards went creak,
I shed a tear and was full of fear,
When from the gloom, green eyes did appear.

Emma Laing (8)
Auchtertool Primary School, Auchtertool

The Seaside

On a hot sunny day at the seaside,
I see cracking crabs, shiny fish and bright shells,
Boys and girls making sandcastles,
Singing songs and swimming in the sea,
Lots of small boats trying to catch fish,
And people surfing,
The seagulls catch fish,
That are thrown over the boats,
It is getting late,
The tide is coming in,
It is no longer noisy,
Everyone is going home.

Scott Fernie (9)
Auchtertool Primary School, Auchtertool

Jack Frost

I have her bed in my sight
And I visit it every night
The window is always open
So I can peek
We play hide-and-seek
On cold nights
I creep under her sheet
And freeze-nip her feet,
I have her bed in my sight
And I visit it every night.

Phillip Duckett (7)
Auchtertool Primary School, Auchtertool

The Lava

The lava is roasting red blood
Bubbling down the street
Flowing fiercely without pity
Melting my world,
The rocks come thudding,
Smashing and splashing
Run faster, run faster,
My world is gone.

Kristoffer Patrick (10)
Auchtertool Primary School, Auchtertool

The Strange Seaside

The grey sea looks like rushing rivers
Late for their work,
The slapping sea sounds like a slippery seal,
In a bad temper,
The salty sea tastes like a very stale chip,
The brown sea smells like an unwashed seagull.

Rebecca Wilson (9)
Auchtertool Primary School, Auchtertool

The Ghost Under My Bed

Every night when I go to sleep
I hear a funny laugh
It doesn't sound friendly
I think it is a ghost
But there's no such thing.
But last night
It came out to play spooky games,
It's a creepy little ghost
And a troublemaker too,
My ghost is invisible,
It pushed me out of bed
It might come back tomorrow,
I am scared.

Deema Chehade (8)
Auchtertool Primary School, Auchtertool

My Pony

My pony is as white as snow
She can trot
But likes to walk slowly
We ride through the woods
Listening to singing birds
And rustling trees
Smelling summer flowers
Hearing buzzing bees
Whisper is my pony
And my special friend
When we are riding
I wish it did not end.

Emma Scott
Auchtertool Primary School, Auchtertool

Windy Dreams

During the night I dreamt
Of heavenly adventures and delights
I met the wind swaying through the sky.

I wondered, *is he a person*
Or a creature hiding from me?
He whispers and dashes, begins to fly,
We have races and dances,
Until I can touch the sky,
It is autumn,
The wind is an Olympic champion,
Running with no control,
My wind has gone,
Where is he?
I am alone,
My dreams have vanished.

Ayesha Siddique (11)
Auchtertool Primary School, Auchtertool

Walking In The Forest

I was strolling in the forest
Suddenly I stopped
I was looking at a tree
The wind was howling in the bitter breeze
The swaying branches were like pointing fingers
Poking down at me,
The trunk was like a giant runway
Reaching to the top of the sky
I stopped and listened and slowly turned
Was that a jet flying to the sky?

Fiona Rennie (10)
Auchtertool Primary School, Auchtertool

Safari Zone

In the wild safari park
I see a chasing cheetah
Hunting a stripy zebra
I hear a roaring lion
Calling for its missing cub
I smell a dung beetle
Rolling in the muck
I feel a hissing snake
Slithering over my bare foot
The cheetah eats the stripy zebra.

Calum Adams (8)
Auchtertool Primary School, Auchtertool

The Shark

I know a shark,
The shark is silvery, slimy,
He shines like a diamond,
It is like no other shark,
A special shark no one can see,
People can't see this shark,
But only inside of me,
Why do I see this shark?
Is it a curse?
It is inside of me.

Mani Siddique (10)
Auchtertool Primary School, Auchtertool

From My Window

The clouds are like cushions,
The sun hotter than flames,
Flowers grow from seeds like children,
Smoke blows like a black sheep's wool,
Swinging and smiling in a world of fun.

Kayleigh Wood (7)
Colinsburgh Primary School, Fife

Olympics

Pain is bright blood-red,
It sounds like a baby crying,
It feels like a weight falling on your finger,
It tastes like sour strawberries that have still to ripen,
It looks like some giant door opening,
It is like someone screaming with fright.

Winning is pink with shock,
It sounds like people cheering for their favourite football team,
It feels like the best thing that's happening,
Winning tastes like grapes that have already ripened,
It reminds people of their favourite things.

Nervous is as white as a ghost,
It sounds like people crying because they're scared,
It feels like pain wriggling down from head to toe,
Tastes like sour apples that no one can eat,
Looks like a black cloud going by in the sky,
Reminds people of thunder and lightning.

Fear is the brightest yellow you can ever get,
Sounds like the scream of a girl,
Feels like cold ice going down the back of the neck,
Looks like someone that just got a fright,
Reminds most people of the worst thing that's happened in their life.

Relief is pink like the person's exhausted,
Sounds like a broken instrument that is still able to play,
It feels like the hot sun,
It tastes like kiwi that's just ripened,
Looks like a pink berry still not ready,
It reminds people of red strawberries.

Sharece Burnett (10)
Colinsburgh Primary School, Fife

The Olympics

Pain
Pain is a black river inside you,
A cat's claws scraping on a blackboard,
It feels like a dagger's piercing you,
Pain tastes like a lump of mud going down your throat,
It looks like a dirty river drowning my emotions,
Pain reminds me of a hole sucking me in.

Happiness
Happiness is a yellow sun in the sky
It sounds like a child laughing excitedly,
Feels like a cold drink on a hot day,
It tastes like chocolate ice cream lying on my tongue,
Looks like a hill of joy,
Reminds me of a day with my friends and family.

Proud
Proud is gold and yellow mixed together,
It sounds like the commentator and the crowd cheering you on,
It feels like you have accomplished something,
You never thought you could do,
Pride tastes of my special birthday cake I made,
Pride looks like a smile you have never seen before,
It reminds me of passing my level C test.

Disappointment
Disappointment is dark brown puddles over your body,
It's a boring history lesson you don't want to hear,
You keep trying and trying but you can't do it,
It tastes like raw egg in your stomach,
Rotting milk in a cup,
Disappointment reminds me of money on the ground
But you can't get it.

Fear
Fear is black like space, ·
It's a scary advert that you can see but you can't switch it off,
Fear is a battle of real and fake,
It looks like your worst nightmare coming to life,
It's a bullet coming towards me in slow motion.

Declan Fielmar (9)
Colinsburgh Primary School, Fife

Olympics

Proud is bright pink like glowing skin,
It sounds like a great yell of *yes*
It tastes like fresh apples,
It looks like a happy face,
It reminds me of painting a colourful picture.

Nervous is bright red like you've blushed,
It sounds like the cold wind passing by,
It tastes like my grandad's cold milk running down my throat,
It looks like lots of people in front of you,
It reminds me of people running in the Olympics.

Pain is like a purple bruise,
It sounds like someone calling for help,
It tastes like a little bit of ice,
It looks like someone crying,
It reminds me of going up a ramp only to fall.

Happiness is like yellow sun waiting for you,
It sounds like people saying you've won,
It tastes like you've done very well to win,
It looks like you've got a very happy face,
It reminds me of a very happy day.

Marc Robertson (9)
Colinsburgh Primary School, Fife

From My Window

The sun is like fire in the sky
The sky like a blue sea around it
The grass a thick forest.

The clouds sit - two white guinea pigs
In their sky hutch.
The wind blows twisty roads towards
Sparkling sunshine.

Kayleigh Dewar (8)
Colinsburgh Primary School, Fife

The Olympics

Pain is the colour red of cold blood,
It's the sound of fingernails scratching the blackboard,
It feels like ten knives have stabbed you in the back,
Pain tastes like my mum's cooking,
Pain is a monster you have made in your head.

Focused is the colour brown like bark off the trees,
It's the sound of the quiet library,
It feels like time has stopped and you're the only one left,
Focused tastes like a cup of tea,
It looks like a book waiting to be read.

Relief is the colour blue of the sparkling sea,
It sounds like giants sighing,
It tastes like chicken nuggets that get stuck in your throat,
Relief looks like the green hills of Mull and the blue skies
Of Iona are in front of you.

Proud is a warm orange sun in your heart,
It sounds like cheering of your spirit,
It feels like your mum's given you the biggest hug,
Proud tastes like warm chocolate running down my throat,
It looks like a proud strong castle that has stood through time.

Determination is the colour yellow of lightning striking down fast,
It is your conscience telling you not to give up,
It feels like the day is never going to end,
Tasting like raw eggs that's making you stronger,
Determination looks like a battle never giving up.

Niall Hutchison (11)
Colinsburgh Primary School, Fife

The Olympics

Successful is like a rainbow exploding in the sky,
It sounds like a boy who has won a bet,
It feels like a pat on the back from a good friend,
It tastes like a well-earned cake,
It looks like a long walk of happiness in the evening.

Relief is a bright green leaf on a summer's day,
It feels like a successful dare,
It tastes like a bowl of fresh salad,
A breath of fresh air escaping from a balloon,
It looks like a long-mid summer's day leaving golden leaves in its
wake.

Determined is like a tropical storm pulling through,
It sounds like a scream at a sword piercing the night sky,
It feels like a baseball clashing through the stadium,
Cold water trickling down a parched throat,
It looks like a castle under siege.

Disappointment is like friendship falling away,
It sounds like someone crying an oath,
It feels like breaking an old record,
Tastes like sour milk on a cold day,
Looks like a sinking vessel on a lone sea.

Pain is like chain lightning flashing through the night sky,
It sounds like the roar of a lion slaying its prey,
It tastes like warm blood painting the ground red,
Pain looks like shining yellow fangs in the starless sky.

Lewis Rabjohns (9)
Colinsburgh Primary School, Fife

The Olympics

Nervous is a dark blue stormy sea,
It sounds like cold teeth chattering,
Nervous feels like you are stuck in a
Blizzard and you can't go on,
It tastes like sour milk left out in the sun,
Nervous looks like a cold windy day,
It reminds you of freezing cold water
You have just jumped into.

Happiness is green in colour,
It sounds like birds chirping on a spring morning,
Happiness feels like a hot summer's day on the beach,
It looks like sparkling shiny water in a stream,
Happiness reminds me of the people who are special to me.

Pain is the colour red,
It sounds like someone screaming for help,
Pain feels like a knife going through you,
It tastes like burnt food in a big kitchen,
Pain looks like blood dripping slowly,
It reminds me of danger lurking round a corner.

Relief is the gold medal round my neck,
It sounds like people cheering in the crowds,
Relief is the cold feel of the metal,
It tastes like a meal you've never had before,
Relief looks like the finish line after the 100m,
It reminds you of staring at the scoreboard
And waiting for your score to come up.

Muscles are the colour red
It sounds like weights hitting the ground
After getting picked up,
It feels like heavy pressure on your body,
Tasting like a strong curry,
Muscles remind me of a famous boxer
In a tense match.

Robbie Provan (10)
Colinsburgh Primary School, Fife

Olympics

Happiness
Happiness is the yellow sun waiting to burst into little pieces,
It is like crowds going wild,
Happiness feels like the wind breezing by,
It tastes like ice cream running down my throat,
Happiness reminds me of doing my best.

Health
Health is pale peach like lounge walls,
It is water settling down at night,
It feels like gold waiting to fall into my cheeks,
Health looks like people running in circles.

Exercise
Exercise is blue like the sky drifting by,
Exercise sounds like hitting walls like feet running by,
It feels the hot, hot sun touching me whilst I tan,
It tastes like chocolate cake running towards me,
It reminds me of bikes riding past.

Proud
Proud is a turquoise-blue as the sea sparkling at me,
It sounds like children running around playing games,
Proud is like waterfall splashing to the ground,
It tastes like sweet strawberries running down my throat,
The sun shining on me and shining through,
It reminds me of everybody taking part.

Winning
Winning is like gold falling on the ground,
It is a crowd screaming at me,
It feels warm like the sun beating down on me,
Winning looks like a hot summer's day,
Tasting like ice cream and sauce running down my throat,
It reminds me of having fun and playing games.

Laura MacDonald (10)
Colinsburgh Primary School, Fife

The Olympics

Winning

Winning's colour is yellower than dazzling mustard,
It sounds like Americans winning lotto,
Feeling like a teddy bear cuddle,
Winning tastes like milk chocolate in a freezer,
It looks bigger than being in Heat magazine,
Winning reminds me of flying free.

Determination

Determination's colour is as red as a rose,
It sounds like the angry growl of a bear,
Feeling like your knuckles are in a cage,
Determination tastes of dried sweat, after running the marathon,
It looks like Kenny Perry giving a speech,
Determination reminds me of the look on a wrestler's face.

Honour

Honour's colour is darker than a tangerine,
It sounds noisier than twenty rock bands,
It feels like fresh potatoes with cheese,
Honour tastes like jam cake with icing,
It looks like Halle Berry winning an Oscar,
Honour reminds me of the world cup.

Muscles

Muscles' colours are bluer than the veins of a river,
And sound like getting punched by a kangaroo one hundred times,
Feeling more powerful than five prime ministers,
Muscles taste like eating a whole horse,
They are like being stung a thousand times by a wasp,
Muscles remind me of the World's Strongest Man competition.

Medals

Medals' colours are golder than the treasure in Treasure Island,
They sound like church bells ringing on a Sunday,
And feel like being buried in chocolate doughnuts,
Medals taste like freshly brewed coffee, keeping you up
                                                    all night bragging.
They look like shiny new buttons on my favourite coat,
Medals remind me of the hottest pizza ever.

Graeme Peebles (11)
Colinsburgh Primary School, Fife

From My Window

Clouds race across the sky as if
they are in the cushion Olympics.
Flowers are like sunbathers
following the sun.
Birds in the sky like rapid
whistles flying from tree to tree.
The sun is a general and the
flowers are his army
around the giant blueberry pond.

Sandy Dunsire (8)
Colinsburgh Primary School, Fife

From My Window

Lightning like sharp glass falling out of the sky,
Black candyfloss rolls across the sky,
Thunder like the armies of Aragorn clashing together,
A hurricane like a twisty roller coaster in the sky,
Trees on fire like Olympic torches.

Connor Hutchison (7)
Colinsburgh Primary School, Fife

The Olympics

Nervous

Nervous is like the blue sky with black clouds nearby,
It sounds like the shaking of shivers,
Nervous feels like butterflies in my tummy,
It tastes like cold ice going down my throat,
It looks like silver raindrops in the sky,
Nervous reminds me of the blowing wind going by.

Pain

Pain is like red juice from a strawberry,
It sounds like a baby crying,
Pain feels like a box falling on your hand,
Pain tastes like sour black berries from the field,
Pain looks like red blood coming from your finger
It reminds me of my granny singing.

Happiness

Happiness is like the sun shining on me,
It sounds like the crowd screaming in your ears,
Happiness feels like a rosebush coming back to life.
It tastes like jelly going into my tummy,
Happiness looks like butterflies flying around me,
It reminds of a winning medals.

Relief

Relief is like the colour yellow lying on the beach,
It sounds like horses neighing,
It feels like having a bath that is going to turn into ice,
Relief tastes like fresh kiwi fruit in my mouth,
It looks like someone has one a medal,
It reminds me of when a girl in France cut down a tree
and it almost hit me.

Fear

Fear is like red blood coming from my head,
It sounds like someone's scream,
Fear feels like a baby crying,
It tastes like ice going down in my tummy,
Fear looks like someone who has had a fright,
It reminds me of my cat fighting.

Nicole Simpson (9)
Colinsburgh Primary School, Fife

The Olympics

Competition is yellow like lightning flashing in front of you,
It sounds like a war in action,
Competition feels like you're being attacked,
Tastes like sandy gravel going down your throat.

Fear is blue like ice waiting to crack below you,
It feels like a bullet to your brain,
Sounds like the crowd booing you,
Fear tastes like worm tablets.

Health is green like very long grass
It tastes like your greens with mashed potatoes,
Sounds like your heart beating fast,
Health reminds me of vegetables.

Connor Wood (9)
Colinsburgh Primary School, Fife

From My Window

I went out in the rain
Thunder and lightning
Zigzags in the sky
Like jaggy glass in
God's disco - flashing lights
And thumping beats.

Bronwen Parker (7)
Colinsburgh Primary School, Fife

The Olympics

Successful is red-hot legs,
Successful sounds like my mum singing,
It feels like being gold,
Successful tastes like the best home-made soup,
Running to the line first,
It reminds me of standing on the podium.

Medals are red-hot gold,
They sound like sparkling songs,
Rock hard gold bumpy and shining,
They taste of sparkling water,
They remind me of that best day at Athens.

Relief is the sun burning my hot body,
It sounds like the best experience ever,
It feels like my body can't move one more step,
Tastes like sour milk been left for months,
It looks like a scary movie,
It reminds me of getting to the end.

Focus is a calm blue sky
It sounds like a quiet song,
It feels like the cool wind in my face,
It tastes of cold ice cream running down my throat,
Looking a mile to the line,
It reminds me of crossing the line first.

Tradition is like white snow,
It sounds like your country's anthem being sung a lot,
It feels like touching the gold medal,
It tastes like hot chocolate falling down my throat,
It looks like all of Britain are at the Olympics,
It reminds me of my family being there.

Andrew Gardner (10)
Colinsburgh Primary School, Fife

Olympics

Pain is like a bursting leg with blood
Like a volcano erupting in front of you
It sounds like you are peddling as fast as you could go
Pain tastes like you are running round the world
It looks like somebody hurt
Pain reminds you of a big red head.

Proud, if you win a medal you are proud
It is like me cheering you on
Like your family wishing the best for you
Proud is like you getting lots of medals
It feels like you winning lots of races.

Nervous is blue ice waiting to crack
Nervous is like the ice waiting to turn into ice cream
It tastes like sour bombs falling into your mouth
It feels like getting jumped on
It sounds like a fast engine going.

Successful is like gold falling in my hands
It sounds like the birds singing
It's like eggs waiting to hatch
It reminds you of scoring loads of goals at the match.

Fear is like birds not even trying to fly
It feels like you jumping off a cliff
It sounds like me on a jet going very fast
It tastes like chillies in your mouth.

Craig Blyth (9)
Colinsburgh Primary School, Fife

Olympics

Pain

Pain is the colour of a freshly picked strawberry,
It sounds like the scream of someone hearing a gunshot,
Pain feels like a kick in the stomach,
It tastes of sour milk flowing through your body,
Pain looks like red ocean whacking against the rocks,
Painful is my dad's singing.

Happiness

Happiness is the colour of sun rinsing in the east,
It sounds like a lost child finding her parents,
Happiness feels like the best thing in the world,
It tastes like a juicy apple sinking into my teeth,
Happiness looks like the sun setting in the west,
Reminding me of a long summer's night.

Disappointment

Disappointment is the colour of the darkest night,
It sounds like the worst music you've ever heard,
Disappointment feels like a kick in the teeth,
It tastes like uncooked prawns clinging to you tongue,
It's a rainy day stopping you from having fun,
Disappointment reminds me of when I lost a race.

Competition

Competition is the colour of athlete's sweat,
It sounds like the cheer of the crowd supporting you,
Competition feels like this is their big chance,
Tasting like glory, light on your tongue,
It looks like the determination on their faces as they run,
Competition reminds me of winning a race at school sports day.

Proud

Proud in the colour of a gold medal,
It sounds like your national anthem,
Proud feels like a hug from your mum and dad,
It tastes like Sunday lunch with all the family round,
Proud looks like happy faces cheering you on,
It reminds me of the sun setting beautifully in the west.

Success

Success is the colour of the shining sun,
It sounds like the sharp call of the owl flying over the moon,
Success feels like you've passed an exam,
It tastes like a posh meal going down your throat,
Success looks like a baby deer jumping across a road,
It reminds me of doing my best.

Charlotte Haigh (10)
Colinsburgh Primary School, Fife

From My Window

Lightning is crashing down like cracked lightbulbs,
Telephone wires lean over like drunken men,
The house is broken like a dog that has lost a bone,
A boulder is rolling like an egg down a hill,
A frog is scared like a child surrounded by fire,
The pond is splashing like a rolling tidal wave,
The bench is sitting like someone lying on their back,
The thunder is as loud as a marching army,
The clouds are as dark as a bowl,
The sky dark like space,
And a duck sets as yellow as a lemon.

Mark Haigh (8)
Colinsburgh Primary School, Fife

From My Window

The night was very scary
It was not hot,
It was cold,
It was freezing!

We had no food
Rain got worse
So . . .
So I left!

Danielle Leitch (8)
Colinsburgh Primary School, Fife

From My Window

The sun is like a flame of fire
The flowers smell like perfume
The grass as fresh as an apple
The river bluer than the sky
Birds sing like a music box
As people walk around.

The clouds are candyfloss painted white,
The flowers grow like the people
And everyone is happy
On this beautiful day.

Margaret McCall (8)
Colinsburgh Primary School, Fife

Energy

Down at the power station
Starts a little movement
As the energy starts to move.

Out he pops through the little gap,
Starts walking towards the tunnel,
Big, powerful and lively as he starts going faster.

Pushing left and right
Around the sharp bend,
Then roaring as he crashes into the sideboard.

'Nearly there,' he says. 'Just up ahead.'
Faster and faster he goes
Until finally he's there.

He uses his strength to get higher,
Round and round he goes,
And out pops the toast!

Jane Bullivant (11)
Craigrothie Primary School, Fife

Animals

Some animals can be cute,
Some animals can have a loud toot,
Some animals can be soft,
Some animals can be cross,
Some animals can easily eat their prey,
Some animals are eaten today!
Some animals can be really fierce,
Some animals can easily pierce,
Some animals can be beaten,
Some animals can be screeching,
Some animals are big,
Some animals can be fat like a pig!

Caitlin Sinclair (8)
Craigrothie Primary School, Fife

The Sun

The sun is a very light fireball,
The sun is playful
But not like you and me
The sun likes to play and jump,
Across the sky,
The moon appears,
It's time for bed soon.

John Bullivant (9)
Craigrothie Primary School, Fife

Waterfall

Flowing down,
Shooting rocks,
Rushing by,
Sparkling blue,
Extraordinary force.
Waterfall!

Ryan Kaempfe (8)
Craigrothie Primary School, Fife

Tractor And Farm

T attie harvesting
R aking
A mazing
C arting
T ractor
O n wheels
R olling

A griculture
N oisy sounds
D angerous

F eeding
A ctive
R adiant
M achinery.

Kyle Andrew Small (9)
Craigrothie Primary School, Fife

Electricity - Kennings

E lectricity
L ife saver
E xcellent energiser
C ooker warmer
T V worker
R adio releaser
I ron burner
C lassroom brightener
I nvisible mover
T ricky transformer
Y ellow lightener.

Sean Alexander Cowan (11)
Craigrothie Primary School, Fife

Sun

Blazing light,
Toasting hot,
Sizzling sun,
Golden heart,
Fire raising,
Sparkling red,
Shining sight,
Bright atmosphere,
Energy giver,
Feet warmer,
Melting away,
Daily disappearance,
Really extraordinary.

Kirsty MacKay (11)
Craigrothie Primary School, Fife

Energy - Kennings

Active mover,
Light bringer,
Food grower,
Strength giver,
Power provider
Bulb brightener,
Life maker,
Force keeper,
Stamina possessor,
Body helper,
Excellent energy!

Brogan Sinclair (9)
Craigrothie Primary School, Fife

The Sun Can Give Me Energy

T oasting
H ot
E nergetic

S unny
U tterly hot
N ever cold

C aring
A mazing
N o giving up

G iver of light
I nspiring
V icious
E ver warm

M aking light
E xciting

E verlasting
N ectarine colour
E xtraordinary
R adiant
G reat
Y ellow.

Fraser Wilson (9)
Craigrothie Primary School, Fife

The Sea

You use energy
Splishing and splashing
You're blue, green and grey,
Some days you are peaceful,
But you can be dangerous and wild,
Boats being tossed and turned
Children gently paddling in you.

Leah Reid (8)
Craigrothie Primary School, Fife

The Sun

The sun is really bright,
Sparkling in the sky,
It looks red and golden yellow,
The light is like a fireball,
Boiling, roasting and toasting things.
The big star up in the clouds making us warm,
It's strange the way it gives us light,
And its shining power is really strong.

Ewan Anderson (8)
Craigrothie Primary School, Fife

The Sun

The sun is a bright shining light,
Sparkling hot in the sky,
Golden yellow in the colourful sky,
You make people smile,
You tan people,
Crops grow in your light,
Energy flows from you,
Brilliant sun.

Jack Wilson (9)
Craigrothie Primary School, Fife

The Sun

Sunlight very warm,
Blazing bright,
Golden yellow,
Makes me happy,
Sizzling hot,
Makes me glad,
Red and orange,
Colours in the atmosphere!

Eve Sinclair (8)
Craigrothie Primary School, Fife

The Black Stallion

Galloping down the fields
He comes,
Sees me bringing his morning yums,
Trotting up the yard he comes,
Soon I start grooming his sleek back coat,
Delicate and soft,
I start to tack him up,
With his shiny black saddle
And his sparkling black bridle.
The moment I've been waiting for
Jumping on a riding away.

Catriona MacKay (11)
Craigrothie Primary School, Fife

Tractor

T here he goes roaring up and down the field.
R eally good engine allows it to keep us up all night.
A good tractor is what we need.
C uts nettles like a flying plane.
T ractors can pull
O r they can lift
R eally good tractors are a gift.

Daniel Henderson (10)
Craigrothie Primary School, Fife

The Sun

It's yellow and bright
And stirring with power,
It will light up the sky,
With its colourful sparkles.
It gives you energy
And grows your food,
The sun is the best!

Caitlin Stewart (8)
Craigrothie Primary School, Fife

I Like Hearing Things

I like hearing many things
Like a buzzing bee
Or whistling of the sea.
I like hearing many things.

I like hearing many things
Like a cat miaowing
Or a dog barking.
I like hearing many things.

I like hearing many things,
Like the wind whistling
Or the sun blazing.
I like hearing many things

But the best sound of all
Is the school bell at three o'clock.

David Andrews (10)
David Livingstone Memorial Primary School, Blantyre

Smelling Things

I like smelling so many things
Little things and big things
Like my little brother's skin
And my bedside air freshner . . .

I like smelling many things
So many things in the world
I like smelling petrol
Even though it can be harmful sometimes.

I like smelling many things
Like my dad's aftershave
I also like the smell of new-made buns.

When I smell things
    It makes me feel
        On top of the world.

Louise Parsons (9)
David Livingstone Memorial Primary School, Blantyre

Smelling Things

I like the smell of many things

I like the smell of rubber rings
I like the smell of petrol,
I like the smell of newborn babies,
I like the smell of hairspray.

I love the smell of many things

I love the smell of scones in the oven,
I love the smell of burned toast,
I love the smell of marshmallows,
And also melted chocolate.

I like the smell of many things

I like the smell of cut grass or new carpet getting laid,
I like the smell of lavender,
I like the smell of food getting cooked when walking
                    past the Chinese takeaway.

If I had a day to smell all my things,
First I would smell my shower gel which smells like coconut.

Laura Vance (10)
David Livingstone Memorial Primary School, Blantyre

I Like

I like smelling a fresh rose
I like smelling babies' toes
I like smelling a teddy's hair
I like smelling a tasty pear.

I like tasting hot coffee
I like tasting sticky toffee
I like tasting tasty curry
I like tasting a Rolo McFlurry.

Nadine Shaban Salim (9)
David Livingstone Memorial Primary School, Blantyre

Smell

I like smelling many things.

I like the smell of petrol,
marker pens and glue.
I like the smell of newborn babies,
hairspray and gel.
I like the smell of tar
freely laid on the ground.
I like the smell of takeaways
when I'm walking down the road.
I also like the smell of fresh-cut grass
and the countryside.

I like the smell of many things.

Blair Armstrong (10)
David Livingstone Memorial Primary School, Blantyre

Smell! Smell! Smell!

I like smelling many things
    like paint
        and aftershave
Sometimes I even like the smell of petrol.

I like smelling many things,
    like the sea
        and food
I also like the smell of cake
    that's just been baked.

But most of all
    I like smelling
        a fresh hamburger.

William Hughes (10)
David Livingstone Memorial Primary School, Blantyre

Happiness

Happiness is like an open blue sky
Letting out fresh air.

It feels like a gentle flower petal
Swishing and swaying calmly.

It looks like a silky flower
Gliding in the fresh air.

It sounds like birds singing
In the treetops.

It tastes like cake,
The sweetest cake you ever tasted.

Rakhsana Ishaq (9)
Garscadden Primary School, Glasgow

Love

Love is like the sun shining
A red rose floating inside you.

It tastes like a hundred strawberries in your mouth,
The taste of love.

It smells like flowers blooming in your garden,
It smells like a red rose.

It feels like Valentine's Day
Like someone says, 'I love you.'

Kurtis Roberts (10)
Garscadden Primary School, Glasgow

Happiness

Happiness is the warm sun shining very brightly
while we are playing in the park.

As red as a rose,
growing in a garden.

It is as lovely as a little bird
singing in a field.

Love is tasty like a strawberry tart
freshly made at the baker's.

Love looks like children playing
happily in the park.

Courtney O'Neill (10)
Garscadden Primary School, Glasgow

Happiness

Happiness is bright yellow flower
It flutters about inside you.

It sounds like a bird singing
Playing with its friends.

Happiness tastes like a bright red apple
It is really juicy.

Happiness feels like a big white fluffy cloud.

Alasdair McKechnie (10)
Garscadden Primary School, Glasgow

Love

Love is strong,
A red sky at night.
Love sounds like a band playing soft music at a church.
Love tastes like candyfloss sizzling on your tongue
on a warm summer's night.
Love feels like a fluffy pillow on a black sofa
with a red bumpy wall.
Love smells like hot cross buns
on a cold winter's night.

Hannah Jenkins (9)
Garscadden Primary School, Glasgow

Love

Love is red
It is like red roses.
It floats about when I am happy,
Love smells and tastes sweet like candy,
It feels like a cloud in the shape of a heart,
It bounces about inside and outside me,
It reminds me of when I was little,
It makes me feel so loving to everyone.
But the thing I love the most is when my mum says, 'I love you!'

Charlotte Gillian Ross (10)
Garscadden Primary School, Glasgow

My Poem Of Excitement

Excited is a sunny yellow colour reflecting in the window.
Excitement is like being on a fluffy cloud.
Excitement sounds like being in a theme park on a summer's day.
Excitement tastes like being in the park eating candyfloss.
Excitement is like strawberry ice cream to cool you down on a hot day.
Excitement feels like having a guardian angel.

Leeanne Robertson (9)
Garscadden Primary School, Glasgow

Happiness

Happiness is like a bright yellow flower,
As yellow as the sun, flaming in the sky.
Happiness looks like a grassy field
With roses and dandelions swaying in the wind.
Happiness tastes of sugar, like candyfloss melting in my mouth.
Happiness smells as lively as a rose,
Like the sea on a fresh breezy morning.
Happiness sounds like a bird twittering away,
Making a dull day as bright as ever.

Beeza Ahmed (10)
Garscadden Primary School, Glasgow

Anger

Anger is as black as night,
Fearless yet scared.
It tastes bitter,
Bitter as a sour grape.
It is rough and hard,
Like a boulder on the mountainside.
It sounds horrible,
Like someone's screaming.
It smells like rotting bodies in a graveyard.

Roísín Vagg (9)
Garscadden Primary School, Glasgow

Happiness

Happiness is like a bright yellow sunshine, warming us on holiday.
It is like getting a new little baby.
Happiness looks like a red rose blooming in springtime.
It sounds like a little bird twittering in the trees,
Happiness smells like fresh air and newly-cut grass,
It feels like being in the airport waiting to go on holiday.

Hollie Boyd (9)
Garscadden Primary School, Glasgow

Happiness

Happiness is sweet, sweet and sugary,
As yummy as a caramel shortcake.
It's as sparkly as the stars at night
And a pretty sunshine-yellow.
It's like a lovely flower
A brilliant yellow daffodil, swaying in a field.
When you feel it, it's as warm as a summer's day.
Velvety and silky, fluttering in your heart.
Happiness sounds like a bird singing
To a cheerful-sounding song.
Happiness is sweet and starry,
You will recognise it, when you feel it.

Rachel Louise Walker (10)
Garscadden Primary School, Glasgow

Love

Love is red and pink,
It smells like roses,
It tastes sweet,
It feels so soft,
And it is very smooth like a newborn baby,
It lives in the deep meadows of my heart.

Somaya Naas (11)
Garscadden Primary School, Glasgow

Happiness

Happiness is white,
It smells like freshly-cut grass.
Happiness tastes sweet like honey,
It sounds like birds singing,
It feels soft and smooth.
Happiness lives in the heart.

Andrew Robertson (11)
Garscadden Primary School, Glasgow

Cheerfulness

Cheerfulness is like bright yellow daffodils
Growing in a field proudly.
Cheerfulness is as fluffy as a white cloud
Floating in the big blue sky.
It sounds like a cool breeze
Wafting through the fields.
Cheerfulness smells like washing
Dried on the line.
It tastes like candyfloss
Melting in my mouth.

Eden Thomson (10)
Garscadden Primary School, Glasgow

Hate

Hate is black,
It smells like burning.
Hate tastes sour,
It sounds like screaming,
It feels like pain.
Hate lives in our body.

Linzi Hamilton (10)
Garscadden Primary School, Glasgow

Hope

Hope is green,
It smells like girls' perfume,
Hope tastes like the fresh air we breathe,
It sounds like fresh-cut grass swaying,
It feels soft and smooth,
Hope lives in the middle of the soul.

Kyle McGeoch (10)
Garscadden Primary School, Glasgow

Love

Love is a bright light,
A light that shines,
Through the whole of your body.

Love is a field,
With pink and white flowers,
Lovely red ones too.

Love is gentle and smooth,
It's full of slow music.

Love is a rainbow,
That shines in the sky.

Love smells sweet,
Like a strawberry-flavoured gel pen.

Love is a pink heart,
That flutters about inside you.

Love is like a diamond,
It's very delicate and sparkles over and over again.

Love is pink,
As pink as a princess's dress.

Love is great
To me and to you.

Gillian Deans (10)
Garscadden Primary School, Glasgow

Hate

Hate is black, very dark black
It smells like burnt tyre smoke.
It tastes like burnt toast,
It feels hot, bumpy and rough,
It lives inside you.

Billy Munro (11)
Garscadden Primary School, Glasgow

Love

Love is a room of lovely red
Filled with roses and hearts.
Smooth and silky to the touch,
Velvety down in your heart.
Love is like Heaven
With angels and blue sky.
Flocks of birds singing
Producing melodious music,
Love is like strawberries,
Covered with frothy cream
With the smell of flowers all around you.

Megan Lee (10)
Garscadden Primary School, Glasgow

Happiness

Happiness is yellow,
It smells like flowers,
It tastes so sweet,
It sounds like laughing,
It feels soft and smooth,
It lives in fun.

Jodie Hamilton (10)
Garscadden Primary School, Glasgow

Love

Love is pink
It smells sweet.
Love tastes like strawberries,
It sounds happy,
It feels soft,
Love lives in everyone's heart.

Samantha MacMillan (11)
Garscadden Primary School, Glasgow

Poverty

Poverty is a worn grey,
It smells like an old musty shoe.
Poverty feels rough and gritty.
It's a quiet, eerie sound but cries out for help at night.
It tastes like rotten veg with a bad after-taste.
Poverty lives on the street and in the back of our minds.

Emma Furie (10)
Garscadden Primary School, Glasgow

Happiness

Happiness is bright green,
Happiness looks like a big long garden,
Happiness is like Heaven,
Happiness is like a stream of water,
Happiness tastes like candyfloss melting in my mouth.

Faisal Byansi (10)
Garscadden Primary School, Glasgow

Love

Love is pale pink,
It smells like a warm summer night,
It tastes nice and sweet like chocolate,
Love sounds like Gareth Gates,
Love feels soft and cuddly like a teddy bear,
It lives deep in the centre of my heart.

Laura Keen (10)
Garscadden Primary School, Glasgow

Death

It is black with death,
Death smells like rubbish,
It tastes disgusting and poisonous.
Death sounds hateful,
It feels sharp and pointy,
Death lives out of love's way.

Andrew Peddie (11)
Garscadden Primary School, GlasgowHope

Hate

Hate is black,
It tastes like something sour and rotten,
It sounds like a hungry lion.
Hate feels rough and thinks it's tough,
It lives some place alone
And you don't want to find it.

Darren Campbell (11)
Garscadden Primary School, Glasgow

Hope

Hope is red,
It smells like air,
It tastes like sweetness,
It feels soft,
It lives in your heart.

Kulbir Gabba
Garscadden Primary School, Glasgow

Death

Death is black,
It smells like rotten egg.
Death tastes sour and bitter,
It sounds like drums banging,
It feels painful.
Death lives in the soul.

Craig Morrison (11)
Garscadden Primary School, Glasgow

Particles

Particles are white,
They smell like fresh air,
They have a taste like vanilla ice cream,
They sound tuneful and feel soft,
They live in the air we breathe.

Sophie Ellis (10)
Garscadden Primary School, Glasgow

Love

Love is red, the colour of blood.
It smells like melted roses,
It tastes like sweet delicious strawberries,
It feels, hot, warm and breezy.
Love lives in the soul.

Jaye Berry (11)
Garscadden Primary School, Glasgow

Tropical Rainforest

T he rainforest is big,
R are are the animals that live in the rainforest,
O ther kinds of animals live in the rainforest,
P oor people live in the rainforest,
I ndian people live in the rainforest,
C olours are wonderful in the rainforest,
A ll the rainforest floor is covered with insects,
L ayers of trees.

R ain falls in the rainforest,
A nimals live in the rainforest,
I t is a big place to live in,
N ever be idle in the rainforest,
F ish are swimming in the ponds,
O ur rainforest is big,
R ainforests are the biggest forests in the world,
E veryone works hard in the rainforest,
S traight trees are in the rainforest,
T rees are very high in the rainforest.

Ann Nicol (9)
Garthamlock Primary School, Glasgow

Tropical Rainforest

T he trees are blowing,
R ain is very hard,
O n the trees are monkeys,
P eople are in the rainforest,
I n the forest animals are there,
C anopy hangs over the rainforest,
A ll rainforests are covered in trees,
L ittle insects run about.

R ainforests are really humid,
A nimals are looking for food,
I ndians hunt everyday for food,
N othing can stop the animals being extinct,
F orest is covered in leaves,
O n the ground are many different things
R est of the animals are feeding,
E verything is hectic
S nakes cling to the trees,
T he snakes eat insects.

Jillian Gray (10)
Garthamlock Primary School, Glasgow

Tropical Rainforest

T he rainforest is a place where animals live.
R ainforests are covered in trees.
O wl monkeys sit on branches.
P eople put feathers on their heads.
I n the forest people chop down trees.
C oatis are very small and crawl on the ground.
A ll animals are different sizes.
L eaf cutters cut all the leaves.

R ainforests are lovely and quiet
A nts go on the green leaves and bite holes
I guanas are green and slimy creatures.
N ine-banded armadillos stay in the rainforest.
F orests are wet and muddy.
O lingos hide behind leaves.
R ed-eyed tree frogs are tiny creatures.
E merald tree boas curl round trees.
S quirrel monkeys jump from one tree to another.
T he topaz hummingbird hums all the time.

Leanne Hendry (11)
Garthamlock Primary School, Glasgow

Tropical Rainforest

T ropical rainforest is hot and cold,
R ain is kept out by the trees,
O ver the canopy are the emergent trees.
P eople have hardly a life in the forest
I nsects carrying their food on their backs
C ould you stay in the rainforest for a day?
A nimals losing their homes to hunters.
L eaves fall over the forest floor.

R esources in the rainforest are very exciting
A n agouti is a champion nut cracker
I n the rainforest there are lots of animals
N ectar is where bees get their food from
F orest floor is the lowest level in the forest
O ver the rainforest there are nice animals
R odent is a small animal like a squirrel
E ndangered means threatened with hunters
S nakes called anacondas kill eagles
T he life in the rainforest is spectacular.

Dillon McGovaney (11)
Garthamlock Primary School, Glasgow

Tropical Rainforest

T rees are huge and very thick.
R ound and round with lots of sticks.
O ver the canopy the emergent trees stand tall.
P lenty of shade covers all.
I nsects run around all day.
C hildren catch them and play away.
A nimals come in different varieties.
L arge and small, all different sizes.

R ed and blue frogs jump about.
A ll the frogs are small and stout.
I nnocent flowers blossom away.
N ice and beautiful colours all day.
F rightened and scared all night long.
O nly the sound of the birds singing their song.
R ound the corner far away.
E merge the men for their prey.
S mall and innocent little fish all for their dish.
T he rainforest, what a life!

Ashley Dailly (11)
Garthamlock Primary School, Glasgow

The Rainforest

T he rainforest is lovely and quiet
R ain falls heavily down on to the ground,
O ut in the country there are lots of them,
P eople that live in the forest make a living,
I nsects live in the rainforest, make homes,
C ommon iguanas climb up the branches,
A ll the animals are different kinds,
L oves the rainforest and also the trees,

R ainforest plants are lovely,
A nd so are the trees,
I n the rainforest animals live,
N ine-banded armadillo sits in a hole,
F orests are all different
O asis hummingbird sings from its heart,
R ed-eyed tree frog sits on leaves,
E merald tree boa curls up the tree,
S nakes are green and slimy,
T ree porcupine sits viciously.

Michelle Reilly (11)
Garthamlock Primary School, Glasgow

Tropical Rainforest

T rees and trees is what it has
R ow upon row and that's a fact
O ver the understory the canopy lies
P lenty of insects and horrible flies
I n the rainforest and rain falls deep
C an you see all the people asleep?
A frican rainforests have lots of plants
L ovely and beautiful, sit and glance.

R ainforests and beautiful
A ll it has is lots of nature
I n a lovely colourful picture
N ature grows very peacefully
F orests and flowers grow weekly
O ver the trees there are lovely birds
R ocking and rolling as they sing
E ast, west nature can fly
S outh, north all the poor creatures die
T rees are the rainforest, help them live.

Jane Cunningham (11)
Garthamlock Primary School, Glasgow

Tropical Rainforest

T rees are tall and small.
R ainforests are very big.
O ver the trees there is a canopy.
P eople visit some rainforests.
I nsects live in the rainforest.
C aterpillars live on the trees
A nts live in the rainforests.
L ight does not get into the rainforest.

R ainforests have loads of trees
A nts live in the rainforest
I nsects are small and big
N obody likes colourful frogs
F rogs are all different colours
O ther rainforests have different animals
R ainforests are full of animals
E lephants do not stay in the rainforests
S nakes live in other rainforests in other countries
T ropical rainforests are beautiful.

Danielle Woods (11)
Garthamlock Primary School, Glasgow

Saturn

S pinning round space
A lways orbiting the sun
T urning and twisting
U ranus its neighbour
R ounding planets, there it goes, a
N itrogen ball.

David Leonard (8)
Killearn Primary School, Glasgow

Neptune

N ear to Pluto
E arth is far away
P erfect blue colour
T urning round and round
U p so high
N eptune's sister Uranus
E verything flies in space.

Niamh Turner (9)
Killearn Primary School, Glasgow

Saturn

S econd biggest planet of them all
A mazing rings go round this ball
T ouring round the sun
U ranus is his best friend
R ockets shooting by
N o one is here.

Flora Matthews (9)
Killearn Primary School, Glasgow

Earth

E arth rolling round
A small, little planet
R ight on its own
T he coolest of them all
H omeward bound.

Kirsty Findlay (8)
Killearn Primary School, Glasgow

Earth

E arth is very fast
A t spinning around
R ound and close
T o the sun
H elping people survive.

Angus North (9)
Killearn Primary School, Glasgow

Pluto

P luto so cold
L ying so lonely
U nable to see the sun
T he distance's away
O range aliens jumping along.

Alexander Russell (8)
Killearn Primary School, Glasgow

Pluto

P luto is the smallest of them
L ike ice as cold as the North Pole
U nable to see the sun
T his is chilly
O range aliens having fun.

Danny Corcoran (8)
Killearn Primary School, Glasgow

Mars

M eteor Mars has no charge
A liens fighting on blood-red Mars
R ockets going around mysterious Mars
S o near the scorching sun.

Calum Norval (8)
Killearn Primary School, Glasgow

Pluto

P oor little Pluto
L ying there by himself
U nderstanding why he's alone
T he neighbourhood lets down the tone
O ther planets never groan.

Louise Bell (9)
Killearn Primary School, Glasgow

Venus

V enus is the hottest planet
E arth is its neighbour
N o sign of life
U nable to land on
S o very close to us.

Jasmine Leung (9)
Killearn Primary School, Glasgow

Mars

M eteors floating by
A liens laughing
R ockets flying around it
S o near the sun.

Fraser Glencross (8)
Killearn Primary School, Glasgow

Mars

M ysterious aliens floating on Mars
A steroids spinning down to Mars
R ockets going up and down in the night sky
S uper Mars to the rescue!

Alan Beattie (9)
Killearn Primary School, Glasgow

Happiness

Happiness is bright blue
Happiness tastes of sweets
Happiness smells of the sea
Happiness is a big smiley face
Happiness sounds like buzzing bees
Happiness feels like soft grass.

Blair Cooper (8)
Killearn Primary School, Glasgow

Love

Love is sparkly red
Love tastes like freshly baked chocolate
Love smells like bright red roses
Love looks like a deep red heart
Love sounds like slow music
Love feels happy.

Kirstie Buchanan (9)
Killearn Primary School, Glasgow

Excitement

Excitement is bright yellow,
The taste of juicy oranges.
Excitement is the smell of new red roses,
It sounds like joy and happiness.
Excitement is enjoyment!

Kirsten Tempest (8)
Killearn Primary School, Glasgow

Anger

Anger is a dark red colour
And it tastes of burning hot toast
And it smells of burning tomatoes.
It looks like children fighting
And it sounds like children shouting.
It feels like hot flames.

Amy McNeill (9)
Killearn Primary School, Glasgow

Joy

Joy is the colour orange,
It tastes like peaches.
It smells like ice cream,
It looks like fun.
Joy sounds like birds singing.
Joy feels like the sun.

Katie Hughes (9)
Killearn Primary School, Glasgow

Fear

Fear is pitch-black,
It is the taste of ash.
Fear is the smell of a cold night,
It looks like a grey cave.
Fear sounds like a torturing scream.
Fear feels cold.

Robert Cowden (8)
Killearn Primary School, Glasgow

Excited

Excited is like a rainbow of colours
Jumping all over the place.
Excited sounds like a little baby's first word,
It tastes like a lovely ripe juicy apple,
It smells like a sweet you are just about to eat,
It feels like a baby's soft little hands,
It reminds me of a baby's first step.
Excited reminds me of someone getting married.

Amanda Jane McEwing (10)
McGill Primary, Bonnyholm Campus, Glasgow

Happiness

Happiness is yellow like the brightest sun,
Happiness is beautiful like a baby's first ever cry,
Happiness is well baked like the biggest chocolate cake,
Happiness is lovely like Gucci perfume on a model,
Happiness is comfortable like freshly shaved wool,
Happiness is a proud moment like a big graduation.

Gemma Reilly (10)
McGill Primary, Bonnyholm Campus, Glasgow

Frustration

Frustration is red like a raging bull's eyes,
Frustration is like a never-ending maze,
Frustration is like when you're nearly done
But you end up where you started.
Frustration is when you try to win but you keep losing.

Gavin Docherty (10)
McGill Primary, Bonnyholm Campus, Glasgow

Happy

Happy is green like grass.
Happy is like laughing,
It sounds like people having fun.
It tastes like cheese and onion pizza
And smells like cheese and onion.
It feels refreshing,
It reminds me of a very sweet drink.

Sean McKinney (11)
McGill Primary, Bonnyholm Campus, Glasgow

Anger

Anger is red like the evening sky,
It sounds like a mighty roar,
It tastes like the most bitter sweet,
It smells like smouldering rock,
It feels like fiery frustration,
It reminds me of burning magma.

Yousif Al-Ani (10)
McGill Primary, Bonnyholm Campus, Glasgow

Happy

Happy is gold like the sun on the sea,
Happy is like playful music blasting in the sunshine,
Happy tastes like the honey in the beehive,
Happy smells like the sweetness of a flower,
Happy feels like the warmth of the sun,
Happy reminds me of my family.

Stuart Beveridge (10)
McGill Primary, Bonnyholm Campus, Glasgow

Happiness

Happiness is yellow like the flowers growing in the fields,
Happiness is like the ice cream van coming,
It sounds like singing through the streets,
It tastes like chocolate cake coming from the bakery,
It smells like sweet toffee fresh from the bag,
It feels wonderful and fun like children playing in the park,
It reminds me of a baby growing up.

Rachael Donaghy (11)
McGill Primary, Bonnyholm Campus, Glasgow

Depression

Depression is like the grey skies that cover the world before it rains.
Depression is the sound of coming home to crying and whining.
Depression tastes like the bitter taste of sherbet lemons.
Depression smells like pepper and all disgusting things.
Depression feels like the hardness of a rock.
Depression reminds me of the lightning that pierces the skies.

Jordan Kilday (11)
McGill Primary, Bonnyholm Campus, Glasgow

Happy

Happiness is yellow like the shining sun,
It sounds like someone singing nicely,
It tastes like a big chocolate cake,
It smells like fresh air,
It feels like good people,
It reminds me of all the happy people in the Cyprus restaurants.

Rebecca Lees (9)
McGill Primary, Bonnyholm Campus, Glasgow

Happy

Happiness is orange flowers growing among the grass,
Happiness sounds like children laughing, running around the park,
It tastes like chocolate cake melting in my mouth,
It smells like someone making delicious home-made bread,
It feels wonderful to be happy,
It reminds me of when I was young singing my nursery songs.

Lisa McLauchlan (11)
McGill Primary, Bonnyholm Campus, Glasgow

Excited

Excited is illuminous like someone has won the lottery,
It sounds like someone saying hooray!
It tastes like ice cream on a warm day,
It smells like a bowl of fruit.
It feels exciting,
It reminds me of moving to Scotland.

Amy McLachlan (9)
McGill Primary, Bonnyholm Campus, Glasgow

Happiness

Happiness is golden like golden coins in a pot,
It sounds like happy dolphins,
It tastes like sweet honey,
It smells like golden candles,
Happiness feels like the sun's on you,
Happiness reminds me of my mum's perfume.

Siobhan Seils (10)
McGill Primary, Bonnyholm Campus, Glasgow

Tiger, Tiger In The Wild

Tiger, tiger what do you eat?
Deer all night that's the treat.
Tiger, tiger where do you sleep?
In the grass that's where I sleep.
Tiger, tiger what's your prey?
Robbing all day.
Tiger, tiger what do you drink?
Water that's what I think.

Angela Teape (8)
Mossneuk Primary School, East Kilbride

The Open Sea

Sea is flowing,
Leaves are moving,
Land is singing,
Boats are sailing,
Clouds rowing in the sky,
Trees are rustling in the wind.

Heather McColl
Mossneuk Primary School, East Kilbride

Hurricane Bert

Hurricane Bert went across the mountains
And went over the sea,
He's swirling water
And cracking land,
He's making a mess.

Ryan Brown (7)
Mossneuk Primary School, East Kilbride

Summer Is Here

Robins singing,
Flowers growing,
Lambs leaping,
Summer is here.
Leaves green,
Plants colourful,
Summer that's how it happens.
People swimming in the pool,
As it gets full.
Swans swimming at the beach,
People singing, it's summer.

Jonathan Aitken (8)
Mossneuk Primary School, East Kilbride

Shining Sea

Sea is flowing swiftly,
Boats rowing clearly,
Clouds move in breeze,
Lighthouses shining carefully,
Wind blowing strong.

Michael Waddell (8)
Mossneuk Primary School, East Kilbride

Hearts And Stars

Hearts are sparkly and lovely,
Stars are lovely and shiny,
Moon is big and bright,
Hearts are bright and beautiful.

Heather Neil (8)
Mossneuk Primary School, East Kilbride

Hurricane Ivan

Birds are dying,
Land is flying,
Houses smashing,
Skies are waving,
Waves hitting Jamaica,
Trees cracking in the wind.

Ewan Gibson (8)
Mossneuk Primary School, East Kilbride

Everything Around Us

Water is still and shining,
Trees are noisily rustling,
Hot sand burning,
Birds gliding through the wind,
Burning sun, steaming as fire.

Connor McBrearty (8)
Mossneuk Primary School, East Kilbride

Lovely Autumn

All bare trees,
Big rustling branches,
Leaves changing colour,
Clouds drifting along the sky,
Breeze on open land.

Katie MacMillan (8)
Mossneuk Primary School, East Kilbride

The Autumn Breeze

Leaves blowing with wind,
Loud leaves crunching on ground,
People walking in the autumn time,
Vehicles zooming on the leaves,
Trees waving in the wind.

Holly Sheen (8)
Mossneuk Primary School, East Kilbride

The Hurricane

Seas are wavy,
Clouds are dark,
Leaves are flying,
Trees are wavy,
Trees are falling,
Cars are floating,
Houses are flooding.

Ross McKechnie
Mossneuk Primary School, East Kilbride

The Autumn Time In Scotland

Some trees are falling,
People collecting leaves,
Kids playing conkers,
White on grass,
Brown leaves falling.

Razak Hunter (8)
Mossneuk Primary School, East Kilbride

Black

Black is the feeling in your tummy after a 2 litre bottle of Coca Cola,
Black is the colour of night when zombies are about,
Black is the shade of darkness like the shadows,
Black is the feeling of the fur on an evil witch's cat,
Black is the feeling of death the Grim Reaper brings,
Black is the sound of the evil dream bats screech,
Black is the taste of horrible liquorice sticking to my teeth,
Black is the colour and feeling in the vacuum of space
Killing you if you don't have a spacesuit,
Black is the shade and colour of a black hole,
Black is the smell of burning smoke drifting in the air,
Black is the feeling of tarmac staining your clothes,
Black is the texture of the bloodthirsty hound's coat,
Black is the feeling of leather and it's my favourite colour.

Calum Ewing-Hepburn (9)
Mount Florida Primary School, Glasgow

Blue

Blue is the feeling of the sky that we don't see very much in Scotland.
Blue is the colour of the Rangers football team that play in Glasgow.
Blue is the colour of the French jotters for school.
Blue is the feeling of Eeyore out of Pooh Bear.
Blue is the feeling of lovely blueberries going down my throat.
Blue is the taste of Slush Puppies going into my mouth.
Blue is the colour of the school dictionaries.
Blue is the sound of rain hitting the window.
Blue is the feeling on a cold winter's day when my body feels cold.
Blue is the taste of candyfloss I buy at the fair.
Blue is the sound of sea dolphins playing in the surf.

Jenna Cook (9)
Mount Florida Primary School, Glasgow

Black

Black is the colour of coldness and death.
Black is the colour of the night, when ghosts and zombies are around.
Black is the feeling of space in which aliens appear.
Black is the feeling of tarmac that is about to crack.
Black is the colour of the witch's cat that fell off her broom.
Black is the sound of an evil hound snarling with yellow greasy fangs.
Black is the smell of burning smoke.
Black is the taste of fizzy Cola rotting my teeth.
Black is the feeling of the black Grim Reaper killing people.
Black is the feeling of leather like sitting on a dead cow.

Ryan Melville (9)
Mount Florida Primary School, Glasgow

Pink

Pink is the feeling of a sunset in the summer sky.
Pink is the sight of my favourite flowers in the sun.
Pink is the sound of the singer that yells on the radio.
Pink is the taste of strawberry ice cream melting in my mouth.
Pink is the taste of candyfloss that I eat at the fair.
Pink is the sound of soft, cuddly pillows when I put my head on them.
Pink is the touch I like best when I snuggle my duvet
And fall fast *zzzzz* asleep.

Rachel Murray (10)
Mount Florida Primary School, Glasgow

Orange

Orange is the colour when the sun is setting in the sky,
Orange is the colour of the inside of a flower that smells on a
summer's day,
Orange is the colour of oranges that are lovely and sweet,
Orange is the colour of the sun that gives you a good tan,
Orange is the colour of a kitten's fur that is nice and soft,
Orange is the colour of orange juice that slides down your throat.

Maxine Cassidy (10)
Mount Florida Primary School, Glasgow

Sky-Blue

Sky-blue is all round especially in the sky
Where everything flies by.
Sky-blue is the colour of the sea
And a reflection of everything that looks into it.
Sky-blue is the feeling of Rangers in the sun
As the supporters cheer for them in the stadium.
Sky-blue is the touch of my pencil with a stationery set.
Sky-blue is the taste of my water bottle
And water in the bottle trickles down my throat.
Sky-blue is the sound of lots of sea
When it squeezes out the water and sprays you wet.
Sky-blue is the sound of chittery birds sitting in the tree
Singing which gives you a warm feeling inside.

Shelley Goldie (10)
Mount Florida Primary School, Glasgow

Blue

Blue is the colour of the night-time sky that
I see out of my bedroom window.
Blue is the feeling of a frozen penguin I watch on TV.
Blue is the feeling of the deep sea that I think of when I swim.
Blue is the taste of a freezing ice lolly that I like to eat.
Blue is the feeling of a fierce shark that swims in the sea.
Blue is the taste of the fresh cold water that
I like to drink on sunny days.
Blue is the sound of the deep sea.
Blue is the colour of Marge Simpson's hair that
I like to watch on TV.

Natalie Kenyon-Alonso (9)
Mount Florida Primary School, Glasgow

Blue

Blue reminds me of Rangers cheering at a football match.
Blue reminds me of the sound of waves at the seaside.
Blue is the taste of blueberry jam on my toast.
Blue is the sound of the sky and when it is windy.
Blue is the taste of a blueberry slush straight from the machine.
Blue reminds me of the taste of blue ink from my pen.
Blue is the colour of our blue dictionary in our school.
Blue of the nice blue swimming pools in Spain.
Blue is my bed covers which are comfy to sleep under.
Blue is my dad's shirt and tie in the morning.

Robert John Whelan (9)
Mount Florida Primary School, Glasgow

Blue

Blue is the colour of the flowing calm sea I like to swim in.
Blue is the colour of the sky where I watch birds fly.
Blue is the colour of your horrible worst enemy.
Blue is the feeling of the taste of ink down my throat.
Blue is the taste of a Slush Puppie I buy at the shops.
Blue is the sound of snowflakes trickling down my back.
Blue is the look of my favourite colour of eyes.
Blue is the colour of dolphins laughing in the sun.
Blue is the feeling of cold on a December winter's day.

Nicola Kennedy (10)
Mount Florida Primary School, Glasgow

Pink

Pink is the scent of roses in the summer,
Pink is the scent of bubblegum popping on my face,
Pink is the colour of kittens' ears,
Pink is the taste of fluffy candyfloss at the funfair,
Pink is the taste of a Refresher fizzing on my tongue,
Pink is the taste of pink ice cream melting in my tummy.

Karen Laycock (9)
Mount Florida Primary School, Glasgow

Blue

Blue is the feeling of cold on a winter's day.
Blue is the taste of an ice pole lovely and cold.
Blue is the taste of candyfloss making my tummy rumble.
Blue is the colour of snowflakes dripping down my back.
Blue is the look of people's eyes shiny and bright.
Blue is the sound of rain tipping and tapping at my window.
Blue is the brightness of our lovely French jotters.
Blue is the taste of our horrible disgusting ink.
Blue is the feeling of millions.
Blue is the touch of pencil lead which you use to colour with.

Sharon Singh (9)
Mount Florida Primary School, Glasgow

Blue

Blue reminds me of the Rangers flag after winning a match.
Blue makes me feel the navy blue sea.
Blue gives me the taste of a blueberry.
Blue makes me remember the calm blue sky.
Blue makes me feel safe on my house carpet.
Blue makes me feel a Slush Puppie melting in my mouth.
Blue reminds me of the band Blue.
Blue is the taste of blue ink from my pen.
Blue reminds me of our classroom door which I come and go through.

Jordan Fong (10)
Mount Florida Primary School, Glasgow

Blue

Blue is the colour of the sunny blue sky.
Blue is the taste of a Slush Puppie running down my throat.
Blue is the colour of my face when I am ill.
Blue is the sound of the sea swaying in the breeze.
Blue reminds me of my fuzzy blue carpet.
Blue makes me cold like ice in the winter.

Emma Lavery (10)
Mount Florida Primary School, Glasgow

Pink

Pink is the look of summer flowers.
Pink is the taste of sweet raspberries.
Pink is the feel of my kitten's nose.
Pink is the colour of my homework jotter.
Pink is the taste of my Ice Blast melting in my cup.
Pink is the sweet taste of candyfloss fluffy and soft.
Pink is the colour of strawberry ice cream smooth and creamy.
Pink is the taste of bubblegum chewy and sweet.
Pink is the colour of a piglet
And pink is the look of Love Hearts sweet and lovely.

Rebecca McGeary (9)
Mount Florida Primary School, Glasgow

Pink!

Pink is a lovely colour on my wall.
Pink is the colour of my bed covers.
Pink is a lovely rose in the garden.
Pink is the taste of my prawn cocktail Walkers crisps.
Pink is the taste of candyfloss in the carnival.
Pink is the feeling of my bedroom.
Pink is my best colour all over my room.
Pink is safe in my mind.

Alix Fleming (9)
Mount Florida Primary School, Glasgow

Blue

Blue is the feeling of an ice-cold Slush Puppie down my neck.
Blue is the colour of a blueberry, yucky stuff.
Blue is the colour of my football team, they are good.
Blue is the colour of my bedroom where I sleep.
Blue is the colour of the sky where I watch planes fly.
Blue is the colour of my favourite football top that is Rangers.
Blue is the feeling of a freezing ice pole shivering down my neck.

Daniel McCalman (10)
Mount Florida Primary School, Glasgow

Purple

Purple is the taste of grapes sliding down my throat.
Purple is the sound of wine bubbling on my taste buds.
Purple is the colour of Helen's folder and pencil case.
Purple is the colour of a rainbow with lots of other colours.
Purple is Mrs Livingstone's favourite colour which she wears
in different clothes.
Purple is the feeling of Barney that I used to watch when I was a baby.
Purple is the feeling of blackcurrant jam on my morning taste.
Purple is the sound of bruising I get with a bang.
Purple is the outcome of the bruising on my sore leg
And purple is my favourite colour.

Lauren Pettigrew (10)
Mount Florida Primary School, Glasgow

Green

Green is the feeling in your stomach when you come off
a roller coaster.
Green is the colour of a long meadow of grass.
Green is the colour of the best team in the world, Celtic.
Green is the colour of the small little pen that my teacher uses.
Green is the taste of my favourite fruit.
Green is the shape of a tree-like vegetable.
Green is the colour of my favourite subject jotter - maths.
Green is the taste of my third favourite kind of crisps -
cheese and onion.

Luke Horne (9)
Mount Florida Primary School, Glasgow

Blue

Blue is the colour of the sky where I watch the birds fly.
Blue is the taste of the cool water I take from the tap.
Blue is the taste of salt and vinegar crisps from the crinkly packet.
Blue is the colour of Rangers football team, they aren't very good.
Blue is the colour of Eeyore my favourite cuddly toy.
Blue is the taste of blue candyfloss from the fair.
Blue is the colour of my school uniform.
Blue is the colour of P6 French books which I write in to.
Blue is the colour of my favourite mammal - dolphins swimming
                                                    in the sea.
Blue is the colour of my water bottle which I drink from.
Blue is the sound of rain battering off the rooftops.

Olivia Pettigrew (9)
Mount Florida Primary School, Glasgow

Blue

Blue is the colour of a nice peaceful sky in summer.
Blue is the sound of the sea crashing on the rocks.
Blue is the sound of dolphins laughing in the water.
Blue is the colour of Lauren's sparkling eyes.
Blue is the feeling of a cold icy scene.
Blue is the colour of the school uniform we wear
In Mount Florida Primary.
Blue is the colour of my favourite type of Slush Puppies
That I drink when I am hot.
Blue is my favourite colour.

Helen Anderson (10)
Mount Florida Primary School, Glasgow

Yellow

Yellow is the colour of freezing lemon lollies.
Yellow is the colour of my brother's mad hair.
Yellow is one of the colours in a fire that glows at night.
Yellow is the yummy potatoes that I mash up with my green
                                        peas at dinner time.
Yellow is the feeling that makes me happy.
Yellow is a beautiful colour in the sunrise.
Yellow is a colour that my friends have in their hair
And yellow is simply my favourite colour.

Kitty Hodgman (10)
Mount Florida Primary School, Glasgow

Red

Red is the colour of blood squirting out of my arm.
Red is the colour of blackcurrant drowning in my stomach.
Red makes me think of aliens taking over Earth.
Red gives me the feeling of the sun burning my skin.
Red gives me the taste of cola fizzing in my stomach.
Red gives me the taste of strawberry candyfloss in my mouth.
Red reminds me of Rome long ago.
Red gives me a burning feeling in my body.
Red gives me the taste of pepperoni pizza.

Scott Gallacher (10)
Mount Florida Primary School, Glasgow

Blue

Blue is the colour of the ocean.
Blue is the colour of the birds.
Blue is the colour of the pencil.
Blue is the colour in my tummy when I taste the feeling.
Blue is the taste of the raspberry Slush Puppie I sip at the café.
Blue is the taste of Smarties I eat from the tube.

Tahir Anwar (10)
Mount Florida Primary School, Glasgow

Sweets

Purple, red, green or blue,
Orange, yellow and pink.
They are made in many colours,
Even more than you think.

Hansel and Gretel in the gingerbread house
Sweets, sweets galore,
There are loads all over the place,
You won't need to ask for more.

Sweets are like the spring,
Sweets are so much fun,
Sweets are like birds
Tweeting in the sun.

The wrappers can crumple,
The wrappers can crunch,
Rip them off and eat the sweet
After dinner or lunch.

In big glass jars they sit,
Oh they do look nice,
Wine gums and bonbons
And even chocolate mice.

On TV shows they make them,
They put the sweets on cakes,
The confectioner always gets it right,
They must take a long time to bake.

Sweets are lovely,
The best thing after food.
Oh I love sweets
They taste really good.

I don't know how people hate sweets
I love them to bits,
I couldn't live without sweets
And neither could you
You must admit.

Caroline Gilday (10)
Notre Dame Primary School, Glasgow

The Rain

The rain comes down in white and blue,
It makes me sad and other people too.

It mainly comes down in autumn and winter,
But you never know when the droplets of water will hit you.

It can get you in storm, snow or sun,
But if it hits you're sure to run.

If you're in the middle of nowhere
And there's nowhere to go,
Put your rain-jacket on
And off you go.

Always carry with you an umbrella,
Just in case,
Even in the boiling sun the heavens can open.

I've been watching the news about Hurricane Ivan
And I'm feeling grateful,
We don't have rain like them.

I love eating chips
On a rainy day,
Feeling grateful for heat, which we have today.

I don't like the rain,
Nobody does,
I wish it would go away
And never come back.

Sean Morgan (10)
Notre Dame Primary School, Glasgow

The Snow Fight

There was a young boy called Joe,
He loved to play in the snow.
He had a snow fight
And got frostbite
And ended up losing his toe.

Alessandro Marini (10)
Notre Dame Primary School, Glasgow

Hallowe'en

Candles in pumpkins, shining out bright,
Ghouls prowl the streets on Hallowe'en Night.
Kids eat sweets, laugh and scream,
It's every child's favourite day,
It's Hallowe'en.

Carving jack-o'-lanterns, giving out sweets
And hearing those cheerful words, 'trick or treat'.
Then the children come in
Dressed as people
You'd never want to meet.

Inside the houses children watch horror movies,
Whether it's 'The Shining' or 'Hallowe'en'
If it's good and scary
Then they're keen.

As the clock reaches midnight all the adults scream
For Hallowe'en Night is over, or so it seems.

Ruaridh Frize (11)
Notre Dame Primary School, Glasgow

Football

Football, football is all I can say,
Football is what I play.
In the early hours of the morning,
In the late hours at night,
I sleep and dream football.

My friends will say I'm football mad,
But deep inside I'm really glad.
The people to thank are my mum and brother,
They have helped me more than any other.

Football is the only meaning for my life,
Yes it's true.
Football, football I like you.

Ché Julienne-Chalmers (11)
Notre Dame Primary School, Glasgow

Autumn

In autumn the leaves fall and the sky glows,
It seems the sun is real,
Smiling at you from up above.

You can hear the birds singing,
The wind whooshing,
The leaves rolling about on the ground,
They fly up twisting and turning into the sky.

All the lovely colours burning red,
Orange and beaming yellow,
All mixing in together.

People wear long bright coats,
Scarves and gloves,
New flowers growing,
What a wonderful sight.
All the trees flowing
From left to right.

Sitting inside drinking tea,
Dipping chocolate biscuit,
Letting them melt in my mouth,
Mmmmmm . . .
What a lovely thought.

Lying in bed with covers tucked on me,
Ahh!
How nice autumn can be.

Kumba Dauda (11)
Notre Dame Primary School, Glasgow

Spring

Spring is when lambs are born,
Summer is when the sun is bursting through the clouds,
Autumn is when leaves are falling off the trees,
Winter is when the snow falls down.

Lauren Reilly (10)
Notre Dame Primary School, Glasgow

Summertime Poem

In summertime the colours are so bright,
With the flowers and the sun,
It's such a beautiful sight.

In the park it is never dark,
The children shout and play
Every single day,
In the summertime.

In the sky
Not one cloud has met my eye.
The sun beams down,
All around
In the summertime.

Because it is so hot,
I do not like to wear a lot.
I wear my shorts and top
In the summertime.

You no longer drive
In this good weather.
You find a friend
And walk together
in the summertime.

We buy some seeds
And watch a show,
To tell us how
To make them grow
In the summertime.

It is so hot we make ice lollies
And go in the paddling pool,
So we can cool,
In the summertime.

Amy Beer (11)
Notre Dame Primary School, Glasgow

Santa

Santa, Santa is big and jolly,
Has a friendly smile that we love.
Always wearing red - he must support Liverpool,
Bush-white beard like a lion's mane.

Low voices, I think,
Not quite sure,
Talks to his reindeers Rudolph, Comet and the rest.

Everything broken
He will fix with his magic touch,
Broken tables without a leg.
Bang!
Mended.

He loves the winter,
Brr! It's cold in the North Pole.
He has snowball fights
With the elves,
Snow's up to his knee.

Huge red coat with white edges,
Red trousers complete the outfit.
A nice wee hat
With a bell
To keep him warm.

He has a famous wooden sleigh,
Seven reindeer pull on the eve of Christmas Day.

There are many Christmas films and TV shows,
Santa likes 'The Snowman'
Only because of the music.

White and red are Santa's colours,
Red coat, white beard, all thanks to Coca-Cola
Who made Santa wear red.

Tor Brooke (11)
Notre Dame Primary School, Glasgow

Fashion - The Catwalk

The skinny models turn for the camera,
Serious and striking, pouting like fish,
Chanel and Prada, Versace and Chloe,
Expensive and stunning, for which people wish.

The click of the camera, the tap of the heels,
Bags, shoes, trousers, jewels and dresses.
The music blaring in the background,
The designs are pretty, some are messes.

The soft texture of the silk,
The itchy angora fur.
Models with thick, silky hair
Which people would die for.

The taste of the Cristal champagne,
The waiters hand around Belgian chocolates,
Caviar on cream crackers is eaten
With truffles and dainty sandwiches.

The designer perfume wafts in the air
And scented candles smell pretty and sweet.

This world is taken over by it,
We all try so hard to look good.
We go on diets, try to eat healthy food
Which all add up to one thing *fashion!*

Holly Leonard (11)
Notre Dame Primary School, Glasgow

My Day At The Seaside

Lovely flowers in gardens,
Beautiful shells at the sea,
Waves go up and down,
Smell of the salty water,
In the sea all the sand in my feet,
I'll remember the beautiful day at the sea
With my family.

Saahirah Mohammed (10)
Notre Dame Primary School, Glasgow

Autumn

Leaves are falling to the ground,
Red, brown, orange are to be found.

Summer has gone, autumn has come,
There are no more green leaves, they are all gone.

The weather is sunny, but cold with a breeze,
It's misty and foggy, so you'll need a fleece.

You'll need to wear trousers or woolly socks,
A heavy jumper, then you'll be warm.

Leaves are falling on the chairs,
Then being blown away by the air.

You can plant new bulbs in autumn
And then they come up beautiful in spring.

Plants are dying,
They come back in spring,
And then they'll look lovely again.

Natalie Bertagna (10)
Notre Dame Primary School, Glasgow

Tennis

Tennis, tennis is a good sport,
Tennis balls crashing into the court.
Powerful serves shooting like a bullet,
The tennis player's hair looks like a mullet.
Cannonballs shooting side to side,
The player's coach barely has any sight.
'Out, out,' the umpire calls,
The players are standing quite, quite tall.
It is two sets all,
Henman and Federer fighting for it all.
Henman hits a beautiful shot
That makes Federer lose and have a really bad fall.

Taylor Kim (10)
Notre Dame Primary School, Glasgow

My Family

I have an uncle called Usher,
He makes me wear some blusher.
He thinks it's cool,
I think it drools
But I have an uncle that's worse.

I have an aunt J-Lo,
She doesn't run a show,
She makes me wear bows
And horrible clothes,
That's the way this family goes.

I have a cousin called Ikky,
When I come home she's sticky.
She saves up money,
They all call her honey,
But I just nick her money.

I have a friend Naveen
Who obviously thinks she's the Queen.
She is a great actor
And has a pink tractor
And that's my friend the Queen!

I have a sister called Make-up
Who has a baby pup
Who's called Buttercup,
Who apparently says, 'What's up?'

I have a brother, No-name
Who always plays the same game.
He turns and he skips,
He runs and he kicks
And he goes by the name No-name.

I have a friend Nyla
Who is so not a liar.
She turns into fire,
You cannot desire
And that's your brain on fire.

Ayesha Mohammed (10)
Notre Dame Primary School, Glasgow

My Classroom

My classroom comes
        with Laliya chatting.
My classroom comes
        with teachers teaching.
My classroom comes
        with the ceiling crashing.
My classroom comes
        with everyone working.
My classroom comes
        with bells ringing.
My classroom comes
        with doors creaking.
My classroom comes
        with Simone staring.
My classroom comes and sets me free
        like a fish in the sea.

Naveen Qureshi (10)
Notre Dame Primary School, Glasgow

Terrible Dream

I'm feeling rather sleepy,
I'm feeling rather rough,
I'm looking like I stayed up late
And didn't sleep enough.

I went to sleep at bedtime
And dreamt all through the night,
But when I woke this morning
I was feeling far from right.
I'm totally exhausted
'Cause I dreamed I couldn't sleep.

Jemma McDermott (10)
Notre Dame Primary School, Glasgow

The War

Guns shooting
And bombs dropping.
Some people scared,
Mums kissing their children
And see them leave for safety.
Sirens everywhere,
Killing people are the Germans,
Sounds everywhere I hear.

Nyala Arshad (10)
Notre Dame Primary School, Glasgow

In The Blizzard

I see a blizzard, white as snow,
It's coming from the earth below,
Lots of air up above, full of laughter and love.
I hear a wolf loud and clear from its little private lair.
I tasted some water nice and hot, like I never took the lot.
I feel some wind in my hair, will it be good in my ear?
I think I hear the call of the old great red deer.

Georgina Dunne (9)
Notre Dame Primary School, Glasgow

Gizme

I have a young guinea pig called Gizme,
who thinks she's a dog but is'nae.
She chases a stick
But she's really quite thick,
She thinks it's a carrot but it is'nae.

Jonathan Sheridan (11)
Notre Dame Primary School, Glasgow

The Wild Horses

I see them every day,
Running and in their play.
I see the foals being born
And running around in the corn.
I see the swift legged colts,
Who seem to fly as they bolt.
I see them from the great hill,
So I can never see the ones that are ill.
They are so beautiful, so wild,
That's why I watch them when the weather is mild.

Ciára Robinson (10)
Notre Dame Primary School, Glasgow

The Hairdresser's Shop

There once was a lady named Dot
Who went to the hairdresser's shop,
She got a weird style
But it wasn't worthwhile
Because her hair looked like a mop.

Nisha Mohammed (10)
Notre Dame Primary School, Glasgow

Rice

R ationed to the last grain
I s very tasty but hardly any
C reates hunger as there is none
E ventually people fight for rice.

Eva Bloice (10)
Notre Dame Primary School, Glasgow

Royal Rap

Once upon a time,
Long ago,
There lived a fair princess,
Don't you know.

And she lived in a castle,
Way up high,
Looking out on the world,
She could touch the sky.

But she wasn't happy,
No she was as sad as could be,
Even though the princes said,
'Won't you marry me?'

Then one day
Who came riding along,
But the real Prince Charming,
Singing this song.

'Princess, Princess,
Beautiful as can be,
Won't you, won't you,
Won't you marry me?'

That made the princess happy,
Very happy indeed.
She said,
'As long as you buy me a necklace
Made from clear diamond beads.'

So they got married,
But as soon as they were wed,
The nasty Prince Charming said,
'Off with her head.'

Now she's dead,
A sad tale I know,
But that's the end
And I gotta go.

Hannah Oliver (9)
Notre Dame Primary School, Glasgow

The Flower

Once I saw a flower
as pretty as pretty
can be. I bent
down to touch
it but it
pricked
me
suddenly
b
l
o
o
d

r
a
n

d
o
w
n

m
y

l
i
t
t
l
e
finger.
When my mum
came out in such a shock
she tripped over a big rock.

Callia Soave (10)
Notre Dame Primary School, Glasgow

Tank Driver

T rust other soldiers or else
A lways look out for spies.
N ot everyone lives today
K ids are very scared.

D irty soldiers still fight today
R ight or wrong they still fight.
I f I was a soldier I would die
V ery few people worship the war.
E veryone is very scared
R unning here and over there.

Kordian Gil (10)
Notre Dame Primary School, Glasgow

Me

M y favourite colour is blue
A nd I like going to the zoo.
R acing is my favourite type of game,
T ravelling can make me sick.
I am good at swimming,
N ot many people hate me.

Martin Scullion (10)
Notre Dame Primary School, Glasgow

Emily

E mily is my name,
M y second name is Burns
I 'm really half French
L ie in on my favourite day
Y awn in school, I am so tired.

Emily Burns (10)
Notre Dame Primary School, Glasgow

Dressing

On went the woollen tights
That itched until you'd cry
But my mum was convinced
That they were a bargain buy.

On went the long green skirt,
The colour's like mushy peas.
Please don't make me wear this Mum,
Please, please, please.

On went the stiff blue shirt
That you could hardly move in.
I couldn't reach and grab in tig
So my point was proven.

On went the polished shoes
Still squeaky, they were very new,
But they were tight and rubbed me too,
I'm sure my heels are black and blue.

I know this stuff can't be called cool
But it's what my mum calls right for school.

Rosie Birchard (10)
Notre Dame Primary School, Glasgow

Worms

I like worms,
They're curly, whirly, swirly, squirmy, slimy.
My mum hates worms
They're curly, whirly, swirly, squirmy, slimy.
Worms are good for soil,
They're curly, whirly, swirly, squirmy, slimy.
I like worms
But I can't see them because they live underground.

Simone Walsh (10)
Notre Dame Primary School, Glasgow

My Best Poem I Have Written

The beautiful sea in front of me,
Fresh air in my lungs,
Fear in the air,
Lovely cold water on a hot day,
Cold water running through me,
I like the seaside now . . .

Philip Law (10)
Notre Dame Primary School, Glasgow

Sitting On The Beach

Waves crashing by the shore,
Salty smell of the sea,
Lots of children playing in the sand,
Fishy taste of the sand,
My soft towel on my back,
I think of going to sleep right now.

Emily Crockett (9)
Notre Dame Primary School, Glasgow

The Blizzard

Blizzard of the hurricane,
Wetness that the blizzard has made,
Blizzard and wind,
Rain of the storm,
Really strong wind,
Blizzard has gone now.

Nicole Rae (10)
Notre Dame Primary School, Glasgow

A Day I Will Remember Forever

Golden sand in front of me,
Smell of candyfloss,
Children laughing,
Seagulls screeching,
Taste of salt in my mouth,
I feel the sun beat down on me,
I love to be beside the sea.
This is a wonderful day for me,
One I will remember forever.

Kerry O'Donnell (10)
Notre Dame Primary School, Glasgow

Garden Lives

Flowers growing in the sun's light,
Fresh air in my face,
Sounds of children playing,
Grass and flowers of the world,
Petals on the flowers,
In years to come I'll see lots more.

Christopher Bland (10)
Notre Dame Primary School, Glasgow

Carnival

Rides passing by when I walk,
People screaming when I pass a roller coaster,
Sweets in my mouth that are melting,
Air flowing past me on rides,
When I am on the roller coaster.

Eva Grant (9)
Notre Dame Primary School, Glasgow

Teeing Off

Golf, golf
It's my thing.
I love to play and practise my swing,
Driver, iron, wood, putter
I love golf . . .
Even though
I played a gutter.

Gennaro Capaldi (10)
Notre Dame Primary School, Glasgow

Cinquain

Showhorse
Very steady,
Faster, jumping, slowing,
Galloping back to the fence fast,
Showing.

Jordanne McMillan (10)
Pathhead Primary School, Kirkcaldy

Happiness

Happiness is yellow like the sun,
Happiness smells like a sweet shop,
Happiness tastes like a Twirl, when you take the first bite,
Happiness sounds like a little bird first thing in the morning.

Robin Hagley (10)
Pathhead Primary School, Kirkcaldy

Trust

Trust trouble alone to answer everything.
Trust, thoughtful, afraid, fearful, wonder.
Trust friends floating in boats.
Trust amusing blind dogs.
Trust a promise to the block.

Kirsty Ray (10)
Pathhead Primary School, Kirkcaldy

Love

Love is like a red heart,
Love smells like a rosy rose,
Love tastes like a juicy peach,
Love looks like melted chocolate,
Love sounds like a fresh breezy wind.

Danielle Johnston (10)
Pathhead Primary School, Kirkcaldy

There Was An Old Man From France

There was an old man from France
Who was invited to a dance.
He dressed as a can
And was hit with a pan
And was never given a second chance.

Demi Roza (10)
Pathhead Primary School, Kirkcaldy

Love

Love is like a beautiful red rose.
Love smells like the sweetest things.
Love tastes like chocolate slowly melting on your tongue.
Love looks like the sweetest thing.
Love sounds like a love poem being read to you with a sweet voice.

Hazel Robb (10)
Pathhead Primary School, Kirkcaldy

Love

Love is red like a rose,
Love smells like holly hanging on a door,
Love tastes like hot chocolate,
Love looks like a heart staring at you,
Love sounds like a drum in your belly.

Brandon Proctor (9)
Pathhead Primary School, Kirkcaldy

There Was A Lady From France

There was a lady from France,
That couldn't help herself dance.
At the flick of her wrist,
She could do the twist
And she cha-cha'd when she had the chance.

Samantha Tait (9)
Pathhead Primary School, Kirkcaldy

Love

Love is red like roses,
Love smells like strawberries,
Love tastes like hot melty chocolate,
Love looks like sparkles in your eyes,
Love sounds like calm waves relaxing on the sea.

Natalie Minick (9)
Pathhead Primary School, Kirkcaldy

Rugby Town Men

Running hard with the ball
To reach the score line
Up and down the field
Looking to pass.
Getting grass stains on your knees,
Ball falling,
Everyone scrambles for it.
Yelling and shouting
When you score a try
Yeah!

Dean McRobert (10)
Rephad Primary School, Stranraer

Rugby

The whistle is blown
run, jump, punch, kick
and head for the line.
Cross the line
a try is scored.
Hooray, hooray!

James McHarrie (11)
Rephad Primary School, Stranraer

Rugby Match

Started by the whistle
We run, sprint, roll
Pass, tap, try!
We slide, touch, throw and score.
Subs run on and off.
The try line is crossed as we score
Some offside, some onside, some both!
Rephad triumph as we win, cheers,
Cries and screams!
We have a penalty -
The winning try!
We cry, 'We are the champions!'
We hold the cup in front of the crowd.
How proud!
We are Rephad Champions!

Blair Forsyth (11)
Rephad Primary School, Stranraer

Rugby

Running, running
with one goal in mind,
get that ball over the line.
Start off slowly,
then speed it up,
try to keep that ball in touch.
Sprint up the sideline,
dart through the middle,
just run until you are tagged.
Pass the ball,
cross the line,
Try!

Stuart Monteith (11)
Rephad Primary School, Stranraer

Rugby

The whistle went
We were off
Towards the try line and the truck we passed
And tackled, towards the line finding a try
Our spirits rise
But wait!
They score as well!
Our hearts fell - come on guys
We can do it!
A pass, a tackle, a try
We've won it!

Andy Lock (11)
Rephad Primary School, Stranraer

Rugby

Watching the game
From the sideline
It was great fun.
When all came to an end
We went back to school
I would go back.

Ian Cowan (11)
Rephad Primary School, Stranraer

Rugby

R unning fast
U p the field
G reat day, went on and on
B ut sometimes unfair decisions, I just kept on
Y elling all day, then we won. Hip hip hooray!

Kirsty Park (10)
Rephad Primary School, Stranraer

Rugby

All kitted out, ready for a challenge,
Onwards towards the field.
How will the other team manage?
The whistle blows, the game has started!
Rephad School all go forward, whole-hearted.
The crowds roar -
The teams soar
Towards the finishing try line.
1-0, 2-0, 3-0, 4
The boys (and girls) are going to score!
Three cheers for the opposition.
At the end of the day, we won -
That's cool.
Hip hip hooray!

Angus Michael Cochrane (11)
Rephad Primary School, Stranraer

Rugby

As the whistle blows
I tapped the ball and pass it on
tackle, tap and pass.
The player runs onside,
sprints to the try line,
tackle, tap and pass.
He dives into the air to catch the ball,
Place it down, it's a try!
The substitute starts to warm up on the line,
he runs onto the field,
tackle, tap and pass.
As the whistle blows,
we give a cheer, and that's
what happened a week ago.

Steven Leek (11)
Rephad Primary School, Stranraer

Rugby

The whistle blows
We start the game,
The players run for the try line.
The passes are made
So are the tackles,
Over the try line.
Cheers are made
Subs come on,
Others come off.
Here we go again -
Getting tired all the time.
Sweaty and panting is how we feel,
As we cross the try line once again.
We're off and on about seven times
With waiting and drinking
Water all the time.
Back on the field
For the very last time.

Erica McGeoch (11)
Rephad Primary School, Stranraer

Rugby

The whistle blew loudly,
The ball flew through the air.
The ball rolled across the grass,
It was really muddy and there was a pass.
Then the tackle was made
With a hard tap.
It was Friday -
A perfect Friday.

Ross Hughes (11)
Rephad Primary School, Stranraer

Rugby

The whistle blows, we've started.
I'm running with the ball,
I get tagged.
I throw the ball to Kim,
She gets tagged.
She throws it to Erica,
She scored!
Me and Kim are off,
But then we score!
Two - nil. We've won!
We're off, but at least we know
That we won.
It's teamwork!

Amy Hastings (11)
Rephad Primary School, Stranraer

Rugby

R unning
U pwards to the try line
G oing for points
B etween the two posts
Y elling for a win.

Alex Halliday (10)
Rephad Primary School, Stranraer

Rugby

R unning down the field with the wind in my hair
U rging my team on
G etting dirty but having fun
B y the way, we're winning
Y es! Yes! Yes!

Christopher Batty (11)
Rephad Primary School, Stranraer

Rugby

When I was at the rugby tournament
Excitement! I was full of it.
As we scored our first try
I began to cry
Hooray! Hooray! Go Rephad go!
We were never beaten
Rephad has great players
You just can't catch them
I began to grin
We were going to win!
Christopher has scored our final try.

James Bell (11)
Rephad Primary School, Stranraer

Rugby

Pass, drop, catch and kick
We're winners, never beaten
Grass on my knees
Mud on my top
Fun tackling and throwing
For every second.

Chloe McCulloch (10)
Rephad Primary School, Stranraer

Rugby Is Fun

Rugby is competitive and lots of fun
If you think it's boring, you're wrong, wrong, wrong.
Running, passing and the most challenging part is scoring a try
Every time we scored, we went yeah, yeah, yeah!

Steven McWilliam (10)
Rephad Primary School, Stranraer

Rugby

R unning fast
U p the field
G reat time we're having fun
B eating the rest, scoring tries
Y elling, yeah, yeah, yeah!

Sorcha Stephens (10)
Rephad Primary School, Stranraer

Rugby

I enjoyed my day at rugby
I had great fun all day long.
Some people found it boring, but they were
Wrong! Wrong! Wrong!
I dodged and threw and tackled and passed
But best of all I scored a *try!*
It made my day
Until it was time to
Go away.

Nicole Leith (10)
Rephad Primary School, Stranraer

Rugby

R unning down the field
U rging myself on
G oing as fast as I can
B y the touch line
Y es! I score a try.

Kimberley Hendry (10)
Rephad Primary School, Stranraer

Love

Love is like a red love heart.
It feels like a teddy.
It sounds romantic.
It tastes like strawberries.
It smells like roses.
It looks like a rainbow.
It reminds me of the blue sky.

Jordan Dalziel (8)
Ruchill Primary School, Glasgow

Happiness

Happiness is red like hearts.
It sounds like my mum.
It tastes like burgers.
It smells like red roses.
It looks like my brother.
It feels like a soft blanket.
It reminds me of strawberries.

Fraser Gray (8)
Ruchill Primary School, Glasgow

Happiness

Happiness is red like a rose.
It sounds like a dog.
It tastes like an apple.
It smells like perfume.
It looks like a cat.
It feels like a fluffy towel.
It reminds me of my mum.

Nicole MacLean (8)
Ruchill Primary School, Glasgow

Love

Love is like beautiful red roses.
It sounds like the birds tweeting.
It tastes like candy.
It smells like perfume.
It looks like Love Hearts.
It feels like soft wool.
It reminds me of romantic films.

Lisamarie Roy (7)
Ruchill Primary School, Glasgow

Love

Love is red, like my heart.
It sounds like *thump, thump, thump*.
It tastes like mashed potatoes.
It smells like roses.
It looks like gold.
It feels like jelly.
It reminds me of money.

Gary Black (8)
Ruchill Primary School, Glasgow

Love

Love is yellow just like cheese.
It sounds like a violin.
It tastes like chips.
It smells like roses.
It looks like my mum.
It feels like a blanket.
It reminds me of money.

Sean Byrne (9)
Ruchill Primary School, Glasgow

Love

Love is blue like the sky.
It tastes like cheese.
It sounds like my favourite pop band, Busted.
It smells like my Bratz perfume.
It feels like silk.
It looks like my room.
It reminds me of my family.

Kelsey Ferguson (8)
Ruchill Primary School, Glasgow

Love

Love is blue like the sky.
It sounds like lovely songs.
It tastes like fish and chips.
It smells like roses.
It looks like my beautiful room.
It feels like a soft blanket.
It reminds me of my mum.

Kristiana Gruda (9)
Ruchill Primary School, Glasgow

Happiness

Happiness is yellow like the sun.
It sounds like the birds tweeting.
It tastes like pink candy.
It smells like fish and chips.
It looks like a brown dog.
It feels like a furry rabbit.
It reminds me of holidays.

Lee Hutcheson (9)
Ruchill Primary School, Glasgow

Happiness

Happiness is yellow like the sun.
It sounds like you're having fun.
It tastes like sweet bananas.
It looks like the bright sun.
It feels like you are having great fun.
It smells like beautiful bright daisies.
It reminds me of sitting on Millport beach
On a nice day.

Jenna Paton (10)
Ruchill Primary School, Glasgow

Happiness

Happiness is yellow like the sun.
It sounds like air.
It tastes like cereal bars.
It smells like flowers.
It looks like joy.
It feels like greatness.
It reminds me of good times.

David Cooper MacLeod (9)
Ruchill Primary School, Glasgow

Love

Love is like a pink heart.
It sounds like my radio.
It tastes like Frazzles.
It smells like ice cream.
It looks like a Love Heart.
It feels like my mum's soft hands.
It reminds me of my sister.

Garry McGregor (9)
Ruchill Primary School, Glasgow

Happiness

Happiness is golden like the morning sun.
It sounds like joy and laughter from friends and family.
It smells like sweet red roses blooming in the flower patch.
It tastes like a cappuccino with extra cream and froth.
It feels like fluffy kittens all snug in a basket.
It looks like children having fun in the park.
It reminds me of my pet hamster called Smokey.

Jade Keegan (10)
Ruchill Primary School, Glasgow

Love

Love is red, like your heart pumping blood.
Love sounds like a band playing flutes.
Love tastes like the sweetness of sugar.
Love looks like polar bears, playing happily.
Love feels very relaxed like you're on holiday.
Love smells like nice fresh air, like in the country.
It reminds me of Blackpool beach in the summer.

William Roy (11)
Ruchill Primary School, Glasgow

Love

Love is peach, like running along a soft sandy beach,
Love sounds like birds singing a sweet song.
Love feels natural and comfortable like a soft, feather pillow.
Love smells like roses and daisies.
Love tastes like a bright green, juicy apple.
Love looks like the sun and a Love Heart.
Love reminds me of being polite and behaving well.

Rheece McCann (11)
Ruchill Primary School, Glasgow

Anger

Anger is dark red
Like the blood of a horrid creature.
It sounds
Like someone very angry howling at you.
It tastes
Very bitter like salt and vinegar.
It feels
Like you're stepping bare feet on needles.
It looks
Like a bull attacking you and there's no escape.
It reminds
Me of my dad shouting at me for doing
Something really bad.

Xhenis Ramaxhiku
Ruchill Primary School, Glasgow

Love

Love is cream
Like the comfy leather sofa in my living room.
It smells lovely, like a sweet chocolate bar
That has just been opened.
It feels like someone touched your heart
The way only you can feel.
It tastes like strawberries with thick cream,
Freshly picked from a bush.
It sounds like a calm waterfall, flowing softly.
It looks like a rose, full of petals that are very healthy.
It reminds me of a beautiful clear blue sea,
In the summertime.

Shannen Gallacher (11)
Ruchill Primary School, Glasgow

Love

Love is like a long field of red roses,
It feels bouncy and soft, like jelly.
It sounds happy and alive, like you're on a new planet.
It tastes sweet and sour, as if you want more.
It looks shiny, like a sparkling crystal.
It smells like cakes baking, with beautiful icing.
It reminds me of a beautiful waterfall, flowing with love.

Rachel Hayes (10)
Ruchill Primary School, Glasgow

Love

Love is red like a blazing inferno,
It sounds like birds chirping in the morning.
It tastes like the juiciest red apple ever.
It books like a beautiful red rose in a crystal clear vase.
It feels as smooth as a piece of flowing silk.
It smells like a red rose blossoming in the spring.
It reminds me of my old puppy called Fudge.

Scott Adams (11)
Ruchill Primary School, Glasgow

Love

Love is pink, like a heart,
It feels like it is beating softly.
It tastes like tomato soup.
It reminds of a rainbow with pink, red and yellow.
It looks really bright and shiny.

Rebecca O'Brien (9)
Ruchill Primary School, Glasgow

Anger

Anger is red like an erupting volcano.
It tastes like an orange that's been in the sun for a time.
It's like a bull stampeding with its nostrils smoking.
It sounds like banging from drums.
It feels like someone cracking their knuckles.
It smells like old seaweed in and out the sea.
It reminds me of my mum and dad when I'm bad
And getting in a row.

Ross Balmer (10)
Ruchill Primary School, Glasgow

Happiness

Happiness is yellow like the sun when it shines its brightest.
It sounds like the song of a bird in the morning.
It tastes sweet like sugar and strawberries on a Monday morning.
It feels like you are flying in the air.
It smells like honey from a bee's hive.
It looks like a bunch of red roses in a vase sitting on the window sill.
It reminds me of my little cousin when she was born.

Sarah O'Brien (11)
Ruchill Primary School, Glasgow

Love

Love is red like rose petals in a big bouquet of flowers.
It sounds like a choir singing romantic songs.
It tastes like honey from a beehive.
It looks like a puppy with big round, brown eyes.
It feels like rich purple velvet.
It smells like fresh roses that have just grown.
It reminds me of someone's big blue eyes and they are cute.

Zoe Crawford (10)
Ruchill Primary School, Glasgow

School

School starts at nine and ends at three
Play time and lunchtime
Are the best times for me.

We do maths, reading and writing
Geography and history
Aren't very exciting.

Much more fun are music and sports
Not so good
Are school reports!

Pupils come to learn their *ABC*
We practise our counting,
1, 2, 3.

It's sometimes good to see your friends
But my favourite time
Is at the weekends.

Lisa Summers (11)
St Cadoc's Primary School, Cambuslang

Laughter

Laughter . . .
Laughter sounds like fast music.
It feels like someone being happy.
Laughter reminds me of my birthday party.
It smells like children splashing in the sea.
Laughter's colour is orange because orange is a bright colour.
It looks like the sun shining.
Laughter tastes like cheese and tomato pizza, yummy!

Jade McGregor (10)
St Dominic's Primary School, Glasgow

Darkness

Darkness sounds like the rattle of thunder after lightning.
It tastes like a spray of river-tasting water.
Darkness feels like a dark corner, with a breeze.
It smells like manure.

Darkness looks like a dark shadowy corner
Covered with cobwebs.

Darkness is the colour black, like the night.

It reminds me of my rabbit being killed.

Dean Jones (11)
St Dominic's Primary School, Glasgow

Sadness

Sadness . . .
Sadness sounds like a person crying when someone dies
in their family.
It feels like a day when your shoulders hang down.
Sadness reminds me of a time when you've got the flu.
It smells like incense on bodies at a funeral.
Sadness is black like a cold, dark night.
It looks like a dull, rainy day.
Sadness tastes like a hot chilli that burns your mouth.

Ashley McBride (10)
St Dominic's Primary School, Glasgow

Happiness

Happiness looks like two angels
sitting on a cloud.

It smells like the sweet perfume
my mum wears.

The colour of happiness is pink
like a baby's bedroom.

It feels as soft as petals on a poppy.

Happiness tastes like strawberry ice cream
on a sunny day.

It sounds like babies laughing
when you tickle them.

Happiness reminds me of two people getting married.

Ashleigh Reilly (11)
St Dominic's Primary School, Glasgow

Fun

Fun feels like a baby,
It is a yellow colour.

Fun sounds like someone laughing.

It tastes like something nice.

Fun smells like red roses.

It looks like something you enjoy doing.

Fun reminds me of the Jeely Piece club.

Dylan Lee (11)
St Dominic's Primary School, Glasgow

Fear . . .

Fear feels as cold as a grave
in the far corner of a cemetery.
It tastes like mouldy lemons
mixed into a pot.
Fear looks like a gruesome ghost,
pale as bony skeletons.
It smells like a burning candle
in a pitch-black house.
Fear reminds me
of seeing my grandad's sister
the night before she died.

Fear is grey like an old stone tomb.

Darren Stewart (11)
St Dominic's Primary School, Glasgow

Fun

Fun feels as soft as a baby's skin.

It is the colour of sunflowers.

Fun smells like red roses in the park.

It sounds like the laughter of children, having fun.

Fun tastes like strawberry ice cream.

It looks like the sun.

Fun reminds me of children.

Andrew O'Brien
St Dominic's Primary School, Glasgow

Excitement . . .

The colour of excitement is luminous yellow
just like the sun.

Excitement smells like the freshness
of the flowers.

It sounds like birds singing a song.

Excitement tastes like popcorn
at the seaside.

It looks like newborn babies.

Excitement reminds me of the fire engine limo
that my friend Dawn had.

Jade Lindsay (11)
St Dominic's Primary School, Glasgow

Love

Love is pink like a rose
growing in the garden.

Love feels good, like
passing your test.

Love sounds like the
wind blowing in your face.

Love smells like a sunflower.

It reminds me of taking
my first Holy communion.

Emma Gavan (10)
St Dominic's Primary School, Glasgow

Fun . . .

The colour of fun is baby lilac
like a Baby Gap jumper.
Fun sounds like the sound of music.
It smells like chlorine from the swimming pool
when you walk into the pool.
Fun feels like the softness
of a sheepskin quilt.
It looks like a water balloon fight
with everyone joining in.
Fun tastes like Dr Pepper when you drink it.
Fun reminds me of the first time
I dived into the big pool.

Kimberley McElwaine (10)
St Dominic's Primary School, Glasgow

My Kind Of Dog

My kind of dog is white and furry,
My kind of dog has a cold slippery nose
and pale blue eyes.
My kind of dog is white and curly
and she never jumps up.
She never bites but always chews
people's slippers and shoes.
She has a bedroom painted pink
with dog bones all over.
She runs about crazily and chases
butterflies, but never
ever bites.
that's my kind of dog,
what's yours?

Ursula Welsh (8)
St Joseph's Primary School, Busby

My Kind Of Pirate

My kind of pirate is tall and thin
When he's around there isn't a grin.
Evil and vicious, cunning and cruel,
Can't you see that he isn't a fool?
Smart and clever, villain forever.
A long red cloak
A moustache to stroke.
A sharp silver hook,
He's really a crook.
He's got a ship without a rip,
He puts his plank through a slip.
To make his prisoners bounce with a trip,
He has a crew and his assistant, Mr Soo.
He's got many secret passages to keep in his prisoners
And he carved a skeleton with some scissors.
He has one secret - he cannot swim,
And he has to keep in a rubber ring.
He's allergic to fish
And not to be, is his wish.
That's my kind of pirate -
Please tell me yours.

Ciara Lawwell (8)
St Joseph's Primary School, Busby

My Kind Of Dragon

My kind of dragon is tall and thin,
She has a beautiful tail with horrible skin.
She is red and breathes fire,
She lives in a tower with horrible powers.
My dragon's skin is not very thin,
It's rough and gruff and ever so tough.
So that's my kind of dragon,
What's yours?

Petrena Marshall (9)
St Joseph's Primary School, Busby

My Kind Of Witch

My kind of witch is small and thin
With a pointed nose like a toothpick or a pin.
She has long brown hair and beautiful skin,
But when her eye's glow red her skin turns green.
And her voice is halfway between a cackle and a croak.

My kind of witch makes spells and potions,
Her usual ingredients are . . .
Fish tail,
Snake skin,
Blood
Spider's legs
Bird's eyes and rabbit's ears
And then she would say -
'Double, double, toil and trouble,
Fire burn and cauldron bubble!'

That's my kind of witch,
What's yours?

Hannah Siobhan Cantley (8)
St Joseph's Primary School, Busby

My Kind Of Beast

My kind of beast is tall and thin
With big black eyes which makes him grin.
He may not seem very frightening
But that isn't all -
He has big sharp teeth and very hairy claws,
If you look in his mouth you'll only see black
But if you look further down
You'll only see bats.

He lives in a sewers which he will never sell,
He loves it very much he'll stay in it all day.
That's my beast, what's yours?

Colin Campbell (9)
St Joseph's Primary School, Busby

My Kind Of Witch

My kind of witch has a pointed nose,
She's tall and thin
and she has a horrible green face.
My kind of witch has a big black cauldron
for putting spells and potions in.

My kind of witch has a black cat called Thunderbones
and she loves him to bits.

My kind of witch loves eating wild pig,
wild flowers, even leaves from the trees
and sour apples.

My kind of witch has a cat as black as the night sky,
My kind of witch has a cat with a little pink nose
that goes splat.
And my kind of witch sleeps all day.
That's my kind of witch,
What's yours?

Kathryn Mesarowicz (9)
St Joseph's Primary School, Busby

My Kind Of Fairy

My kind of fairy is slender and tall,
With a sweet little smile she looks after us all.
She is small and delightful, she never frowns,
At night watch her wings glitter as the sun goes down.
Her voice is as gentle as the gentle breeze,
That sways against the green-leafed trees.
Her blonde hair sweeps down like a beautiful veil,
It's as long as a white unicorn's tail.
She is as small as a newborn and as young as me.
She is as gentle and caring as can be.

My fairy is dressed in a soft lily-petal gown,
Her shoes are made from eiderdown.
She has a glowing acorn ring,
Her necklace is made from pearls on a string.

Kathryn Mahon (8)
St Joseph's Primary School, Busby

My Kind Of Fairy

My kind of fairy is the size of my thumb,
Whenever I call I know she will come.
She has long straight hair
That is golden and fair.
That's why I call her Sugar-Plum.
Her sapphire-like eyes
Are bright and wise.
Her ruby-like mouth sometimes tells lies.
At night into bedrooms she creeps,
Treasure sometimes she keeps.
But in its place she leaves a surprise.
She lives in a sea-cave lit with gems,
Where mermaids pause to splash with friends.
She has a white horse
Whom she nicknames Norse.
Her wings sparkle at night,
Under the moonlight.
Which shines so bright.
She wears a silk dress,
And her friend made it for her -
She's a gloworm called Jess.
In the hour of darkness and gloom
She weaves a charm around the moon.
That's my kind of fairy,
Please tell me about yours.

Lucy Caldwell (9)
St Joseph's Primary School, Busby

My Kind Of Witch

My kind of witch is villainous and treacherous
With long glossy brown hair.
She has a voice like an angel but a mind like a devil.
And she wears an amethyst on her ring.
Children will follow her because of her soft voice.
When she gets them they will never see the light of day again.

She lives in a cave with her cat, Thundertube,
They will plot evil plans together.
My kind of witch will sleep in a dusty old bed
With cobwebs, dust and cat fur all over it.

In her cupboard she will have lotions and potions . . .
Super hot red chilli sauce,
Frog liquid and fried bats' eyes in water.

My kind of witch would eat . . .
Wild pig, sour apples and leaves and insects.

That's my kind of witch, what's yours?

Kelsey Comerford (9)
St Joseph's Primary School, Busby

My Kind Of Witch

My kind of witch is thin and tall
and ugly and stupid with a big black ball.
Eating worms and slimy slugs she can gobble them up
without even munching,
Which would really keep her prisoners up and crunching.

She lives away from anyone else
her house is messier than a pigsty.

That's my kind of witch,
What's yours?

Victoria Caldwell (8)
St Joseph's Primary School, Busby

My Kind Of Fairy

My kind of fairy's eyes are nice,
They are crystal blue,
Some people say they are diamonds,
They twinkle so much.
Her cheeks are a rosy, pinky-red, kind of mix.
So soft, that's her skin.
Her hair is as black as can be,
Just slightly wavy and so soft.

My kind of fairy is a loveable one,
She is always relaxed.
Such a sweetheart, that's really her.
She walks round helping everyone,
And talks to them about any problems.
Such a helpful little thing,
Helping everyone she sees without
A happy grin.

That's the nice kind of fairy I like -
What's yours?

Amanda Devlin (8)
St Joseph's Primary School, Busby

My Kind Of Devil

My kind of devil is fiery red
and very evil.
He lives in *Hell!*
It's a rocky and cruel place.
He's very violent with a spiky red tail
and sharp horns.
He can breathe fire and drink blood.

That's my kind of devil,
What's yours?

Neale Waugh (9)
St Joseph's Primary School, Busby

My Kind Of Sorcerer

My kind of sorcerer
is tall and slim
with an evil laugh
and a croaky voice.
He is very rude
and very nasty.
He is a vicious,
heartless, cruel, cold-blooded man.
He lives in a dark dungeon
with a dark blue cloak
and his evil pitch-black
dragon called Skarmor.
It is a huge dragon
with gigantic wings with
holes in them.
It has a gold hoop through its nose.
and it has huge fangs
like deadly daggers.
It has to have a chain
round its neck because
it is so vicious.
He plots wicked deeds of what to do
with his evil potions that are
most deadly to you!

That's my kind of sorcerer.
Tell me, what's yours?

Jack Henry (9)
St Joseph's Primary School, Busby

My Kind Of Vandal

My kind of vandal is very clever,
He's always out and about when no one is around.
He's rude and conceited, sinful and violent.
My kind of vandal smashes windows and steals things,
Always unjust, he also does graffiti
And sets off stink bombs.
If you talk to him, he will batter you hard!
He has broken out of jail and all the rest of it.
He wears a jacket, he likes showing his tattoos.
They say that he fled from home on September the 5th,
He lives by himself in the barn on the hill.
They say he does all this to survive,
Or maybe he likes doing it!
He's never kind,
His celebration is war.

That's my kind of vandal, what's yours?

Sean Merrick (8)
St Joseph's Primary School, Busby

My Kind Of Vampire

My kind of vampire is tall and thin,
He has a white face and eyes, dark red.
He has black hair and a cloak as well.

He has very sharp teeth with blood all over them,
He is wrinkly and dark and he is evil.
He has ghostly ghosts
And skeletons to slave for him.

He drinks people's blood and eats meat.
At night he turns into a bat and flies around the sky.
He goes into bedrooms and drinks their blood
Then he goes into his coffin until it is night again.

That's my kind of vampire, what's yours?

Connor McKeown (8)
St Joseph's Primary School, Busby

My Kind Of Witch

My kind of witch is young and pretty,
tall and thin with long black hair that is smooth and sleek.
Her face is white, like a blanket of snow
with lips the rosiest red.
Her voice is angelic and saintly,
with an innocent face and a heavenly smile.
You wouldn't know that she was vile.
Her eyes are blue like sparkling streams.

She knows many spells
and owns many potions.
With crockle dust which makes a smell
and sinkel goo which opens up Hell.
She has enough potions to have a city of flying pigs.

She may look like an angel but inside she's a devil.
Trust me, you don't know the half of it.
Her house is number six, Grundle Street.

Her house is a tall mansion,
with long dark halls and gloomy walls.
That's my kind of witch, please tell me about yours.

Rachel McCallum (9)
St Joseph's Primary School, Busby

One Cold Windy Night

Noises coming from cats and bats,
Street lights flickering,
Hear Mum and Dad laughing,
Hear the wind blowing,
The water whoosh, whoosh,
The washing machine rumbling and tumbling,
The floorboards creaking,
The trees and leaves swishing,
The dogs' howling and cats' prowling,
Then it's morning and nice and bright.

Jerrylee McGowan (9)
St Mary's RC Primary School, Stirling

I Felt Scared

On a cold windy night,
The wind was blowing and whistling
Tree branches were hitting my window.
Outside lights were flashing from the
Racing cars skidding on the road.
I felt scared.

Horns peeping, car doors slamming
People shouting and arguing.
Windows smashing,
Street lights flickering on and off
I felt scared.

Cats crying
Bats squeaking.
Foxes rummaging in bins
Dogs making howling sounds
On a cold windy night
I felt scared.

Nico Burns (10)
St Mary's RC Primary School, Stirling

One Cold Windy Night

Early to bed at night,
Dogs howling,
Cats prowling during the night,
Bats squeaking out the back,
Floorboards creaking,
Emergency sirens blasting,
Fast cars zooming,
Motor bikes fleeing round corners,
Music blaring from cars,
Foxes raking in bins,
Lids blowing and banging about the streets,
Cans rolling,
Trains rattling down the track.

Ryan Watson (10)
St Mary's RC Primary School, Stirling

One Cold Windy Night

Bats squeaking out of sight,
Bats, bats out at night,
You might just get a fright.

Swaying trees making scary shadows,
Rustling and creeping like monsters
In your bad dream.

Wolves howling at the moon,
Voices from the darkness,
Whispering and echoing.

Dogs howling, scaring cats,
Car horns and tyres screeching
Like ghosts in the cold windy night.

Paige Kilbane (10)
St Mary's RC Primary School, Stirling

One Cold Windy Night

Washing machine swishes at night,
Lights outside seem very bright.
Doors squeaking when you're asleep
In your bed at night.
Creaks from the old dark shed,
Ceiling leaking,
Stairs creaking.
Bright moon outside in the night sky,
Bright stars where the bats fly.
Trees rustling,
People hustling.
These are the noises -
I heard in my bed.

Corrina Hamilton (9)
St Mary's RC Primary School, Stirling

One Cold Windy Night

Dogs howling at cats,
Trains rattling the track,
Leaves rustling,
Doors banging,
Floorboards creaking,
Bats squeaking,
Cats hissing,
Foxes rummaging in bins,
Noises from the television,
People talking outside,
Emergency vehicles' sirens blasting,
Puddles turn to ice,
Frost covers windows,
It's a cold windy night.

Nathan Logan (9)
St Mary's RC Primary School, Stirling

One Cold Windy Night

The street lights are flickering,
People are bickering,
Rabbit thumping its feet,
A cat scaring him in the street.
Teenagers fighting in the park,
Time to go home, it's very dark.
Spooky noises coming from outside,
Perhaps from the slide or the old shed.
Trees rustling at my window,
Foxes bustling at the bins.
Scary noises in my bedroom.

Leonie Coyle (9)
St Mary's RC Primary School, Stirling

One Cold Windy Night

Street lights flickering,
Noises from cats and bats,
Floorboards creak and squeak,
Bats' wings flapping and slapping,
Washing machines rumbling and stumbling,
Cars going past in puddles,
The foxes rummaging in bins and tins,
Trains going past on the track, click-clack,
Emergency vans going past my window,
Music blasting from cars,
Owls hoot and toot,
Tin cans rolling down hills.

Amanda McMinn (10)
St Mary's RC Primary School, Stirling

To The Rescue

Emergency vehicle sirens
Blasting, blaring.
Fire engine lights
Flashing brightly,
Fleeing around the streets.
If there is a call
The firemen are always ready.
Wind howling,
Rain pelting,
Thunder roaring.
Car accident!
Emergency services to the rescue!

Logen Ludwig (11)
St Mary's RC Primary School, Stirling

One Cold Windy Night

Floorboards creaking,
Wind whistling,
Dogs howling,
Cats prowling,
Lights flickering,
People chattering,
Moon glittering,
Doors squeaking,
Owls hooting,
Trees rustling,
Traffic roaring,
Trains vibrating,
River thundering,
Bed creaking,
Me sleeping, zzzzz.

Caitlin Robertson (11)
St Mary's RC Primary School, Stirling

One Cold Windy Night

Foxes howling at night,
Prowling,
Rummaging for a bite to eat,
Bats slapping their wings,
Rats squeaking and twitching,
Floorboards creaking,
Thunder banging,
Trees blowing,
Shadows moving,
Loud voices of people
Arguing and shouting.

Kim Lynch (9)
St Mary's RC Primary School, Stirling

One Cold Windy Night

One cold windy night I heard speaking,
Then rats squeaking.
Dogs are howling,
Cats are prowling.
Bats are squeaking,
Cars screeching.
Leaves rustling,
Floorboards creaking.
I saw the moon,
I heard the owls hoot.,
The wind is speaking.
Lights flickering,
Torches clicking.
Tree branches breaking,
Leaves are crackling.
Cars skidding,
They are racing.

Louise Watson (11)
St Mary's RC Primary School, Stirling

At Night

At night bats fly about.
Foxes rake boxes and garbage cans.
When you sleep you'll hear them squeak.
On your own they'll give you a fright.
Floorboards creaking on the stairs.
Noise from the television.
Mum and Dad talking and nagging.

Marc McGowan (11)
St Mary's RC Primary School, Stirling

One Cold Windy Night

In my bed I could hear my floorboards creaking,
Outside there were bats squeaking.
I also heard dogs howling,
I think they caught the cats prowling.
Music from cars,
Shouting from bars.
That night when I was lying in my bed I heard
The door swing on the garden shed
So I went down to the garden shed,
And what did I feel?
A bang on the head.
I woke up the next morning
And I wasn't in my bed,
I was lying on the floor
Of the garden shed.

Stephen Lewis (10)
St Mary's RC Primary School, Stirling

The Wind

The colour of the wind is
A black smoky kind of grey.
The wind swirls like a whirlpool
Whooshing everything around,
Destroying everything in its path.
The wind is as angry as a lion.
The wind howls like a wolf.
The wind roars like a dinosaur.
The wind squawks like a cockatoo.
The wind can blow trees, bins, sand and sea.
The wind can blow umbrellas and people away.

Caitlin Elliot (9)
St Michael's Primary School, Moodiesburn

Colours

Red is like blood coming out from a cut
Or a red juicy apple coming straight from a tree
Or maybe the colour of your head on a hot day.

Blue is like the Atlantic Ocean, ice-cold, freezing
Or the colour of the sky on clear day
Or maybe the colour of the Earth.

Green is the colour of the harvest fields
Or the freshly cut grass of a football field
Or new spring grass.

Orange is an orange freshly squeezed on a hot day
Or even the roasting hot surface of Jupiter
And also the colour of an Irn Bru bar.

Gold is the sun golden and scorching
Or golden wheat sprouting from the soil
Or maybe even a pound coin buttoned up in your pocket.

White is the colour of snow on the roofs
Or the colour of a tiger's whiskers
Or the colour of the clouds in the sky.

Silver is a tear coming from your eye
Or the ink coming from a silver ink pen
Or the colour of a pencil case.

Andrew Cairns (10)
St Michael's Primary School, Moodiesburn

The Wind

The wind strongly goes up the hill making a terrible noise,
It is thrashing and bashing in the street.
The wind twirls off windows,
Banging and clanging of the metal trash bins.
The wind is prancing in the air,
The street cats get frightened of howling and growling,
The leaves and branches have been blown away,
It even sounds like a werewolf.

Caitlin Fleming (8)
St Michael's Primary School, Moodiesburn

Colours

Red is spurting blood coming out from a wound,
Or the fallen autumn crispy leaves that have fallen off the giant trees,
Or maybe even juicy red strawberries.

Blue is a wavy, freezing ocean,
The cloudy blue sky that covers you,
Or maybe even the deep blue of fascinating Uranus.

Brown is the long, stiff tree stump,
The delicious melting chocolate by the fire,
Or maybe even the light brown haystacks.

Green bright grass that shakes with the wind,
The leaves that dangle up in the trees,
Or the beautifully grown fields.

Yellow is the mouth-watering bananas,
Or the bright beautiful daffodils,
The faraway in the night sky stars.

Black is the colour of the black cats,
Or the black hole in space.

Orange is the colour of the burning sun,
The tickling of the sand,
And a juicy peach ready to eat.

White is the colour of cats' whiskers,
Or a big, cold, hard snowball.

Declan Fitzsimmons (11)
St Michael's Primary School, Moodiesburn

The Weather

The streaking, roaring wind
Rustling through the trees
And angrily rattling the bins
And suddenly, *bang!*
The bin falls over,
The wind is like a scary ghost.

Lauren McLelland (8)
St Michael's Primary School, Moodiesburn

Colours

Blue is like clear-crystal water on a hot summer's day
or a beautiful cloudy sky surrounding us today.

Red is like a big juicy apple just about to fall
or a crackling fire in a little cottage below.

Yellow is like the moon and stars lighting up the sky
or a flickering candle burning so bright.

Green is like crunchy grapes and a crispy harvest field.

Gold is beautiful sunlight beaming down all day
or hidden treasure dug deep down in the sand.

Brown is like big trees blowing in the autumn wind
and leaves splashing about everywhere.

Pink is like a lovely rose in the cold soil
and its long stem is standing up very proud.

White is snowdrops on Christmas Day
with a little robin sitting on a tree.

Rachael McPake (11)
St Michael's Primary School, Moodiesburn

The Wind

Wind, wind spinning and blasting,
Dragging the sand to the coast.
Hurricane, hurricane moving the bin this way
And that way, we go mad.
The wind flashing loudly with squawking and sucking,
Spitting and roaring.
Wind, wind pulling the door as you move indoors.
Storm, storm sucking swiftly, dragging the people
With their umbrellas like Mary Poppins.
Wind, wind coming down the chimney making it noisy,
Making it miserable.

Derek Marr (9)
St Michael's Primary School, Moodiesburn

Colours

Red is like flames dancing around coal.
It feels like scorching desert sand.
It sounds like a burning fire on a winter's day.

Lilac is like juicy grapes just been picked from a field of many others.
It smells like a desert flower's scented perfume.
It feels icy and cold.
It sounds like the howling of a wolf.

White is like the snowdrops on a winter's morning.
It feels like soft white tiger's fur.
It sounds like the roar of a tiger defending their families.

Pink is like a sunset sky on a summer's day.
It smells like a delicious hot meal.
It tastes like sweet pink raspberries.
It sounds like a girl singing a merry song.

Black is like a night sky with no stars.
It feels like coal, rough and lumpy.
It is like a dead fire.
It is like someone crying.

Aynsley Murphy (11)
St Michael's Primary School, Moodiesburn

Colours

Pink is sticky bubblegum sticking to your teeth,
Or tasty candyfloss sticking to your fingers.

Yellow is the lightning that lights up the sky,
Or big long bananas.

Red is a juicy, crunchy apple going into your watering mouth,
Or when a dog licks your hand you can feel its red, rough tongue.

Orange is a juicy, sour orange,
Or the scorching hot sun.

Blue is the clear blue sky,
Or the ice-cold, crystal ocean.

Michelle Taggarty (11)
St Michael's Primary School, Moodiesburn

The Wind Man

The wind is a man
He is grey and white
Sometimes he shouts loudly
I better beware
Do not try to annoy him
His anger could cause
A whirling hurricane
With a roaring sound
Like a lion
But in the inside
He has a soft heart
He lives in a tree
He looks in and out of windows
He goes on a bus
He's like a shadow
Following me.

Eilidh Swinton (8)
St Michael's Primary School, Moodiesburn

Colours

Red is so scorching hot like the blood
After a war has been fought.

A polar bear is cloud white
Just like an angel rising in the light.

Yellow is the colour of spring,
Sunflowers, buttercups, anything.

Black's like a robber strolling in the night,
It's a scary colour, it might give you a fright.

The ocean is crystal blue
Like a bluebell that just grew.

My favourite colour is gold,
It's rich, sparkling and bold.

Aiden Connolly (10)
St Michael's Primary School, Moodiesburn

Colours

Pink is my favourite colour,
It looks like a flower just entered in a vase,
It feels like warm, fluffy pillows on top of my bed.

Red is like a big juicy apple,
It feels like scorching sand,
It sounds like a crackling fire on a winter's night.

Yellow is like a long banana,
It is warm like a big yellow sun,
It shines like a yellow-gold ring.

Orange is like a yummy orange,
It looks and sounds like big fiery flames,
It also looks like a big scary tiger.

Green looks like a big bunch of grapes,
It smells of spring grass,
With flower stems on it.

Purple is my second favourite colour,
It reminds me of grapes, flowers and
Big purple lollipops.

White is like the midnight moon,
With tiny little stars,
By day, white fluffy clouds.

Shannon O'Hara (10)
St Michael's Primary School, Moodiesburn

Autumn Is . . .

Autumn is when birds fly south
Autumn is conkers on the trees
Autumn is when days are shorter
Autumn is September, October and November
Autumn is when flowers die
Autumn is a peaceful time.

Antonia Dick (7)
St Michael's Primary School, Moodiesburn

Colours

Red is like scorching hot desert sand,
Burning flames in the crackling fire,
Apples hanging from an apple tree,
Mars in space all red, no other colours added,
A delicious red strawberry waiting to be eaten.

Blue is like the crystal-clear sky,
The cool, blue pool water sparkling in the sun.

Yellow is like the daffodils swaying from side to side
On a winter's breeze,
The street lights on until dark fades away,
Bananas hanging high up in the trees in the African jungle.

Green is like the crisp gold grass in the fields,
The moss stuck to the rocks never coming off to wander,
A thousand acres of fields and grass in the countryside.

Pink is like a big, fat pig who's just come out of a swamp of mud,
The pink lilies in our gardens.

Orange is like the orange highlights in the sky at night,
The petals of a sunflower stand tall
And straight in the golden sunshine.

Gold is like the golden treasure at the end of every rainbow
Waiting to be found,
The golden sunshine shining in a summer's day.

Kayleigh Fleming (10)
St Michael's Primary School, Moodiesburn

Autumn Is . . .

Autumn is when leaves fall off the trees
Autumn is Hallowe'en when witches come out and children go
trick or treating
Autumn is Bonfire Night
Autumn is when Jack Frost comes out to play
Autumn is when animals hibernate
Autumn is the best time of year because it is my birthday.

Liam Ross (6)
St Michael's Primary School, Moodiesburn

Colours

Red is like a hot midsummer's afternoon
With the sun burning in the sky it feels like a hot burning fire.

Blue is like the clear water of a lake
It feels as cold as ice.

White is as white as the snow at Christmas
It feels like ice melting in your hand.

Black is as dark as the underground with no light
It looks darker than two in the morning.

Yellow is the streetlights at night
Or like a banana that's just ripe
It tastes like a big long banana.

Gold is like a one pound coin just newly made
It looks like money and wealth.

Silver is like a teardrop of joy falling down your cheek
It's like silver rain running down your face.

Mark Kiernan (11)
St Michael's Primary School, Moodiesburn

Colours

Silver is like ten pences flying through the air
and shining like the moon in the night sky.

Yellow is like bananas hanging off a palm tree,
like a baby chick being born and streetlight flickering in the dark nights.

Green is like crusty leaves falling from a tree.

Pink is as tasty as candyfloss and as chewy as bubblegum
getting thrown from side to side in your mouth.

Orange is the colour of the hot steamy sun sitting in the sky.

Blue is as clear as the sea and as cool as a swimming pool.

Red is as runny as a river and tastes like a crusty red apple
being crushed in your mouth.

Erin Pender (11)
St Michael's Primary School, Moodiesburn

Colours

Red is a crunchy, juicy apple eaten on a warm summer's day,
Flames dancing in a burning hot fire,
Or the scorching hot sand in the desert.

Blue is the crystal clear sea surrounding an exotic island,
The clear sky on a hot day.

Yellow is the beautiful bright daffodils,
The tasty bananas in the trees high above,
And the burning hot sun.

Green is all the disgusting vegetables your mum puts on your plate,
And all the crisp moist grass that covers thousands of acres of field.

Orange is the lovely sky at night when the sun is setting,
It tastes of delicious orange juice for breakfast,
And the bright and cheerful lilies in your garden.

White is the rooftops on Christmas Day,
And the big furry polar bears playing in Antarctica.

Gold is the treasure at the end of the rainbow waiting to be found,
The crown placed upon a queen's head,
The coins gleaming in the sunshine,
Gold is also my friend's lovely golden fair hair.

Melissa Johnson (11)
St Michael's Primary School, Moodiesburn

Autumn Is . . .

Autumn is when squirrels gather nuts
Autumn is when animals hibernate
Autumn is pumpkins, orange and fat
Autumn is a witch with her big black cat
Autumn is when children collect conkers
Autumn is fireworks exploding in the sky.

Hannah McInally (7)
St Michael's Primary School, Moodiesburn

Colours

Red is scorching hot like the unbearable surface of Mars,
like the crackling fire on a cold winter's day,
like the burning sand in the hot Sahara desert.

Blue like an ocean, swaying back and forth on a windy day,
like the bright blue sky on a hot summer's day.

White like the cotton candy clouds that always look so delicious,
like a ghost floating on a snowy day,
like a blank piece of paper waiting to be written on.

Gold like a shiny moon on a starry night,
like a pound coin that blinds you by shining against the sun.

Black like a silky undetected cat on a dark night,
like a dark sky on a dark night with no stars to make it bright.

Yellow like the sun glistening on a bright day,
like tasty bananas freshly taken off a tree,
like corn put on a brightly cleaned cob.

Silver like the shining jewellery that you put around your neck,
like a sharp fence that you climb when you're in a hurry.

Jack Berry (10)
St Michael's Primary School, Moodiesburn

The Wind

The wind is a man blowing with force.
The wind is a wolf howling in the night sky.
The wind is like a cold icicle slipping down your spine.
The wind is a strong force howling through the leaves.
The wind is stronger than a rock,
It blows the trees making a lot of racket.
Wind, wind always causing trouble.
The wind loudly interrupts games.
The wind squawks loudly and annoys people.
Wind, wind blowing gates, blowing bins, blowing people,
Blowing them all angry with force.

Paul Slaven (9)
St Michael's Primary School, Moodiesburn

Colours

Red is a juicy apple just picked off a tree,
Or flames dancing and twirling in the fire;
Scorching hot sand in the calm desert.

Blue might be the sea in a dream island,
Or the cold water running from a new fitted tap;
The clear sky on a hot summer's day.

Yellow is the fresh sour taste of a lemon,
Or bananas hanging on a tree high above.
Yellow daffodils swaying in the strong wind.

Green could be the vegetables placed on your plate,
Or the crispy green grass that fills the thousands of acres.

Orange is the sun beating down on us
Or the juice of an orange being squeezed into a cup;
The sky as the sun begins to set.

Pink might be a piglet rolling in the brown, dirty mud.

Gold could be the treasure hidden deep below,
Or the piles of coins gleaming in the sunlight.

White I think looks like snow lying on rooftops,
Or ghosts on their nightly haunt.
White is the Siberian tiger's whiskers.

Laura Kelly (11)
St Michael's Primary School, Moodiesburn

Autumn Is . . .

Autumn is when flowers die
Autumn is when black cats fly
Autumn is when leaves turn orange, brown, red and yellow
Autumn is when swallows go away
Autumn is frosty.

Teigan Jamieson (7)
St Michael's Primary School, Moodiesburn

Colours

Black is the outline of a person lurking in the shadows,
A room never been entered before,
A glass of Coke fizzing away.

Blue is the great Atlantic ocean's thrashing waves,
The beautiful sky above,
Little Pluto from the eye of a telescope.

Green is a football field before a match,
A field where the cows and horses graze.

Gold is the colour of corn before it gets cut,
It is the colour of a wedding ring,
The first autumn leaves to fall.

Red is the nebulum in deep space,
A fire blazing nearby.

Brown is the bark from a tree,
The autumn leaves crispy and fragile,
The colour of our new school uniforms.

Orange is the sun on a hot summer's evening,
A newborn fox so soft and furry.

White is the ghosts that haunt Bedlay Castle,
The kittens' whiskers, so soft and firm,
A stallion grazing on the mains.

Yellow is the hay in the fields after being cut,
A chick in the start of its life.

Michael Myers (11)
St Michael's Primary School, Moodiesburn

Autumn Is . . .

Autumn is when animals hibernate
Autumn is when witches fly on their broomsticks
Autumn is when birds fly away to hotter countries
Autumn is when you go trick or treating
Autumn is when you dress up.

Megan McNicol (6)
St Michael's Primary School, Moodiesburn

Thunderstorm

(Inspired by 'Waterfall' by Cynthia Rider)

T hunderclouds roar
H isses and roars as the night goes by
U mbrellas blowing upside down
N ot a single person in sight
D readful noises through the night
E choes in the wind repeating over and over
R attling a chain through its teeth
S nake of black clouds rise in the sky
T he rain came heavily and fell in floods
O ceans of rain floods the streets
R ivers and lakes roar like beasts
M orning's arrived, the sun is out, thunder's gone away
                       so let's go out and play.

Michaella Johnson (9)
St Michael's Primary School, Moodiesburn

Thunderstorm

(Inspired by 'Waterfall' by Cynthia Rider)

T hundering at night when we are in bed
H urry up and get inside
U mbrellas turned upside down
N ever go outside
D own comes the lightning from the sky
E verybody is holding onto things
R unning away very scared
S nuggled in bed
T hunder and crashing at night
O ceans of rain flood the streets
R attling an iron through his teeth
M ums and dads are not shopping.

Stewart Hendry (9)
St Michael's Primary School, Moodiesburn

Thunderstorm

(Inspired by 'Waterfall' by Cynthia Rider)

T oo many clouds to count, there were about 1,000,000
H orrendous rain in the sky that comes down
U nder my roof I can hear it rumble all day
N obody outside in the horrendous rain
D ogs outside in their kennels today
E veryone stuck in the house, bored with nothing to play
R oaring black clouds thundering up in the sky
S tones are whistling around everywhere
T hunder is going away from here
O h, it's gone away thank you God
R ain is away and now it's sunny
M aybe it might come back again.

Calum McKinnon (8)
St Michael's Primary School, Moodiesburn

Thunderstorm

(Inspired by 'Waterfall' by Cynthia Rider)

T he rain came heavily and fell in floods
H isses and roars as the night goes by
U mbrellas blowing upside down
N ot a single person in sight
D readful noises through the night and
E veryone is scared
R ivers and lakes roaring like wild beasts
S nuggled up inside, nervously scared
T he mountains suddenly lift their trunks to the heavens
O ceans of rain flood the streets
R attling an iron chain through its teeth
M orning arrives and the sun is out, the thunder's away
                                                    so let's go out.

Dionne Johnson (9)
St Michael's Primary School, Moodiesburn

Colours

Red is like a juicy apple
It is that bright it looks like the sun
The fire crackling when the coal is about to be lit.

Yellow is like the sand on a hot day
Bananas melting on that hot day
As the sun settles away.

White - as cold as snow on a tiger's strip
And like the paper we get to draw on
And the ghost that haunts us for the night.

Blue is like a pool, cool and deep
People in planes in the lovely blue sky.

Brown is like the crusty leaves that fall off the tree
And like the branches that lie on the floor.

Orange is like a nice juicy orange
And sunset falls down and hides away.

Multicoloured - the cars as they drive smartly down the road
And the rainbow when it rains.

Pink is like a pig rolling in the mud
And pink mini sports car on the road.

Katie Flaherty (10)
St Michael's Primary School, Moodiesburn

Autumn Is . . .

Autumn is morning mist
Autumn is when Jack Frost comes creeping
Autumn is when it gets colder
Autumn is Hallowe'en
Autumn is when the leaves change colour
Autumn is carved pumpkins
Autumn is my little sister's birthday.

Aidan Lochrie (7)
St Michael's Primary School, Moodiesburn

Colours

Red is the flames dancing in the fire.
Red is the sun beating down on you.
Red is blood coming from your gash.

Gold is the glittering treasure on the seabed.
Gold is the sand on the beach going past your toes.
Gold is a fresh field of crops swaying in the breeze.

Blue is the ocean where the shark waits.
Blue is the sky where the falcon glides.

Brown is the tree swaying in the wind.
Brown is the mud from the downpour of rain.

Black is the background of space with stars as spots.
Black is the thing that surrounds you at night.

Green is the freshly-cut grass.
Green are the leaves falling from the trees.

White is the falling drops of snow.
White is the colour of paper we use at school.

Yellow is the sour lemon hanging on the tree.
Yellow is the banana the monkeys eat.
Yellow is the potato fresh from the field.

Grey is the lead in your pencil.
Grey is the sky on a cold, windy, rainy day.
Grey is the hair when you are old.

Ross Clark (11)
St Michael's Primary School, Moodiesburn

Autumn Is . . .

Autumn is exciting
Autumn is when leaves fall off the trees
Autumn is wonderful
Autumn is when it gets colder
Autumn is fun.

Danielle Corrigan (7)
St Michael's Primary School, Moodiesburn

Colours

Black is like a black hole in space as it sucks in planets and stars.
Black is the colour of space in the never-ending universe.
When the night is black it's cold and damp.

Orange is a fruit - the ripest on the tree.
It is the colour of a fox as it smartly stalks its prey.
The colour of the cheerful sun as it heats up.
The colour of orange makes everyone warm and happy.

Blue is the colour of the sea commanded by Neptune.
Cold and wet as you plunge in the sparkling blue
                              of never-ending colour.
Hear the thunderous roar of the sea pounding off the rocks.

Green is the colour of the leaves of the large, proud tree
                              as it holds against mighty winds.
The colour of the sparkling green grass as it sways in the wind.

Red is the colour of fire as it rips down forests and jungles.
It feels warm as it rummages through villages and towns.
The smell of blood shed in a war.

Brown is the colour of the tree's bark as it stands tall.
The screaming of the tree as it is burnt gives off a terrible sound.
And now the tree falls because of the woodcutter.

Murray Crossan (11)
St Michael's Primary School, Moodiesburn

Happiness

Happiness is red like a ruby.
It sounds like the tingle in my heart.
It smells like a big bunch of roses.
It looks like my mum's smile.
It feels like my heart heading towards home.
It reminds me of my dad.

Lauren McLeish (7)
St Michael's Primary School, Moodiesburn

Colours

Red is a juicy apple, freshly picked from a tree,
It feels so hot like scorching sand,
And sounds like crackling fire just great for a stove.

Yellow is a newborn chick just come out of an egg,
It is a big banana hanging from a tree,
And the sun as hot as a fireball.

Gold is the moon glowing in the night,
And the glowing of a pound coin,
Maybe a lamp post flickering in the night.

Black is the night sky,
And a burglar running into the night,
Or coal just about to light.

Blue is a pool, deep and cool,
Or the sky on a summer's day,
And the blueness of my friend's eyes.

Brown is the new buttered toast,
And brown crunchy leaves falling from a tree,
Or a fox escaping from a farm.

Aydan Topping (10)
St Michael's Primary School, Moodiesburn

Happiness

Happiness is gold like lovely honey.
It sounds like it is thundering.
It smells like my lunch.
It looks like my auntie's hair.
It feels like I am thinking today.
It reminds me of my bird singing.

Jamie Quate (8)
St Michael's Primary School, Moodiesburn

Colours

Black is a burglar lurking in the shadows of the night,
A dark dungeon crawling with rats,
Space which no one can see.

White is the clouds that float about the sky on a nice sunny day,
The cliffs that lie beside the roaring sea,
The crisp snow that lies thick on the ground,
The dusty chalk getting dug out of the pit.

Green is the grass being sprinkled with weedkiller,
The fields of crops like an army of little soldiers.

Orange is the colour of the flames as they dance about a fire
on a cold winter night,
The colour of a goldfish as it swims about its tank.

Blue is the colour of the sky on a warm, sunny day,
The colour of a river as it crashes off the rocks like a glass smashing.

Gold the colour of pound coins when they clatter onto the table
when you're emptying your bank,
The colour of sand dunes as they mount high.

Red is the colour of roasting tomato soup on a cold day,
The colour of a juicy apple dropping from a tree.

Paul Brennan (10)
St Michael's Primary School, Moodiesburn

Happiness

Happiness is like a burning yellow sun high in the sky.
It sounds like bees buzzing in my garden.
It smells like a beautiful baby's face.
It feels like a baby's wee hand.
It reminds me of my little cousin.

Laura Friel (7)
St Michael's Primary School, Moodiesburn

Colours

Brown - a crispy leaf falling from the tree,
a tree trunk so still and quiet,
school uniforms on children walking down the hall.

Red - a crispy apple, so juicy and sweet,
a scorching fire with the flames dancing,
red rosy lips on the face of a friend's face,
a ball shining in the sun.

White - snow is crispy and icy,
a cat's whiskers so wet and cold.

Yellow - a banana, smooth and shiny,
the scorching sun shining in the sky above,
ten yellow pencils shining in the sun.

Green - like a small bean ready to be eaten,
like the smooth long grass
light and bright like a dark splash of green paint on a piece of paper.

Black - like a dark suit, the sky at night, like a blackboard.

Blue - like a clear sky, a pair of blue eyes, a dark wave over the sea.

Pink - pink rosy cheeks like a pink rose blooming from the ground.

Declyn Emslie (11)
St Michael's Primary School, Moodiesburn

Happiness

Happiness is like a ball of fire burning in my heart.
It sounds like the sweet whistling of the birds.
It smells like lying in a bed of roses.
It looks like paradise.
It feels like freedom.
It reminds me of going on long happy holidays.

Ryan Kelly (8)
St Michael's Primary School, Moodiesburn

Colours

Red is a juicy apple hanging from a tree.
It's like a scorching desert.
It is that hot, it is like a fire crackling.

Yellow is the roasting sun on a summer's day.
It is like a newborn chick in a nest.
It is like bananas hanging from the sky.

Gold is like the moon glowing in the night.
It is like the lights flickering on and off.
It is like the treasure deep below
And it is light glowing through the keyhole.

White is like the lion's whiskers
And is like the snow falling.
It is like a person standing like a statue.

Blue is like the sea surrounding an island.
It is like the clear blue sky.
It is like the blue of a rainbow.

Robert Gracie (10)
St Michael's Primary School, Moodiesburn

Autumn Is . . .

Autumn is Hallowe'en
Autumn is Bonfire Night
Autumn is conkers, shiny and bright
Autumn is when animals hibernate
Autumn is fun
Autumn is colder
Autumn is exciting
Autumn is the best.

Declan McKean (7)
St Michael's Primary School, Moodiesburn

Colours

Yellow is like the hot sun on a summer's day,
a candle flickering in the dark.

Gold is the cool sand at the beach
or shiny money.

Orange is the hot flames of a fire,
a sun setting in the sky,
a fox running away in the night.

Blue is like the freezing sea,
the sky on a summer's day.

Silver is like the crescent moon,
rain battering off the window.

Red is blood oozing out of my cut,
a red delicious apple,
the red planet called Mars.

White is the cold snow,
the ashes of a dying fire,
ghosts on a midnight haunt,
a snow tiger walking through the bitter snow.

Black is like the night sky,
a lucky cat,
coal about to burn.

Green is green grass,
beautiful trees,
juicy kiwi fruit.

Brown is autumn leaves,
my school uniform.

Pink is chewy bubblegum,
sweet candyfloss or a small piglet.

Shannon Love (11)
St Michael's Primary School, Moodiesburn

Colours

Red is like a giant juicy apple just waiting to be eaten,
Or a crackling fire burning all around you,
Or even the red-hot sun on a beautiful morning.

Yellow is a watery, delicious banana,
And also a leaf falling from a tree in autumn,
Or maybe even a wall of flame catching you in a mist of smoke.

Blue is like the salty clear sea,
Or a lovely blue sky in summer,
Perhaps even the beautiful planet Neptune.

Black is your shadow following you everywhere you go,
Or maybe even the sky at night,
Or even a black cat lurking about.

Silver is like the luminous glow coming from the moon at night,
Or a ten pence rolling around the floor,
Or even a very bad hailstorm.

Gold is like a piece of treasure inside a sunken ship,
Or could be a very shiny pound coin shining in the moonlight's glow,
Even a necklace on a girl's neck.

Jon Devlin (11)
St Michael's Primary School, Moodiesburn

My Little Brother

My little brother is six years old
My little brother never does what he's told
My little brother is ever so funny
My little brother loves toast and honey
My little brother likes to play ball
My little brother drives my mum up the wall
My little brother likes to scream and shout
My little brother always shouts out.

Emma Rodgers (10)
St Michael's Primary School, Moodiesburn

Colours

Red is like burning flames dancing all around.
It feels like scorching hot desert sand.
Red tastes like a juicy, crunchy apple.
It sounds like a burning fire on a scorching hot day.

White is like dry ashes of fire lying all around.
It feels like snow falling from the sky.
It smells like red burning fire.
It looks like a dump yard with white dust lying.

Green is like harvest fields with new, long, spring grass.
It smells like the grass has been cut.
It's like a parrot's tail.

Orange is like the bright scorching sun.
It feels scorching hot and when you look up at it
It will blind you.

Yellow is like cats' eyes glowing in the dark.
It smells of new fresh grass and it is all muddy.

Gold is like treasure under the deep blue sea.
It is in a big, old, wooden treasure chest.
It had gold coins lying in amongst the jewels.

Michelle McCabe (11)
St Michael's Primary School, Moodiesburn

Me

I live in Bridge Burn Drive
And I have small greeny-blue eyes
I like cats and dogs, birds and frogs
And I love to shop for shoes and clogs
My sister calls me the gossip queen
Because everyone's news I can glean
But I don't care what they say
I'm happy to go my own way.

Kirsten MacFarlane (9)
St Michael's Primary School, Moodiesburn

Colours

Blue is a big pool of water or an ocean roaring
Splashing and crashing to the razor-sharp rocks
Or a beautiful blue sky on a silent spring day.

Red is a crackling fire with flames dancing all around
A crunchy apple ready to be bitten or a scorching desert sand.

Yellow is the bright sun or a candle flickering, burning bright
A bunch of bananas hanging from trees
A newborn chick in the still spring.

Silver is like tears running down an unhappy face
The raindrops on a rainy day or a crown on a princess' head.

Green is the growing grass in spring
Or a mighty jungle covered in trees
Or a bundle of leaves falling to the ground.

Brown is a big tree trunk or a melting chocolate by the fire
Or our school uniform that looks so smart.

Black is a dark night sky or a black cat creeping in the streets
Or coal in a fireplace.

White is snow falling on the ground everywhere
Ghosts on a nightly haunt or tigers' white whiskers.

Gold is glistening coins, sunshine all day
Or the big moon and stars shining so bright.

Pink is like the pink panther or candyfloss that is yummy
Pink tastes so nice you can eat it, especially pink bubblegum.

Nicola Murray (10)
St Michael's Primary School, Moodiesburn

Thunderstorm

(Inspired by 'Waterfall' by Cynthia Rider)

T he moon comes out, the mountain is dark

H iding here and there

U p rushes the storm a moment

N ot anyone out to play

D estiny is closing in

E very night hiding under my covers

R attling an iron chain in its teeth

S nuggling with my dad, frightened

T he mountain suddenly lifts its trunks to the heavens

O ver and over the sea I hear the waves

R umbling off the ground I can feel

M onstrous clouds in the heavy wind.

Kate Hardie (9)
St Michael's Primary School, Moodiesburn

Thunderstorm

(Inspired by 'Waterfall' by Cynthia Rider)

T hrashing and crashing it goes on and on

H ouses will fall to the ground

U nder my bed I feel nervous and scared

N othing to do, everything to fear

D rains fill up and flood the place

E xtremely strong is the thunderstorm

R attling like an iron chain

S ounds of hate, and on it goes

T hunderclouds rend the air

O ver it lights but you can't see bright

R oaring it goes like a wild beast

M oving around in the dark sky.

Victoria Lowe (9)
St Michael's Primary School, Moodiesburn

Thunderstorm

(Inspired by 'Waterfall' by Cynthia Rider)

T hrashing its way across the sky
H orribly scaring children and parents
U nder the bed, frightened to death
N ervously I hide
D ark and fierce, making you feel cold and gloomy
E lectric shock that can kill you
R ain coming down heavily and falling down into floods
S nake of black spitting venom into puddles of danger
T he rumbling wind rattles like a wild beast
O ceans of rain flood the street
R attling an iron chain in its teeth
M onsters rent the Earth.

Staci Brady (9)
St Michael's Primary School, Moodiesburn

Thunderstorm

(Inspired by 'Waterfall' by Cynthia Rider)

T hunderclouds roar
H isses and roars as the night goes by
U mbrellas blowing upside down
N ot a single person in sight
D readful rumbles shake the ground
E choes in the wind repeating over and over again
R ain pours down in a rattling noise
S cary sounds all over town
T hunder and lightning tore the sky
O ceans of rain flood the street
R ivers and lakes roar like wild beasts
M orning's arrived, the sun is out, thunder's away so let's go out.

Lisa Marie Mitchell (9)
St Michael's Primary School, Moodiesburn

Thunderstorm

(Inspired by 'Waterfall' by Cynthia Rider)

T he storming, thrashing thunderstorm
H undreds of clouds passing nearby
U mbrellas blowing everywhere
N o one dares to go out anywhere
D rawing back the curtains on the window, seeing the thunder
    just makes me shiver
E veryone hides under their bedcovers
R ain comes down as I kick a puddle
S torming and roaring, I start to get angry
T ree houses all fall down
O f course, I start to faint and frown
R attling, roaring all about
M e and my parents can't wait till the morning.

Conor Lochrie (9)
St Michael's Primary School, Moodiesburn

Thunderstorm

(Inspired by 'Waterfall' by Cynthia Rider)

T he roaring, thrashing thunder
H iding from the storm
U nder my covers I shake with fear
N eeding a cuddle to feel safe
D own comes the pouring rain
E veryone wants to stay indoors
R ain keeps falling more and more
S naking lightning in the sky
T hunder roaring louder still
O utside so wet and miserable
R ainclouds overhead rolling by
M y fear is over, the storm has died.

Claire Gallagher (8)
St Michael's Primary School, Moodiesburn

Thunderstorm

(Inspired by 'Waterfall' by Cynthia Rider)

T he sun stopped shining and the wind blew
H eavy rain flooded the streets like a river
U nder my bed I hid, scared and still
N ot a soul outside, not even a mouse
D anger everywhere, even if you just stepped out the door
E lectric lightning like lasers in the sky
R ages of anger as if the clouds were fighting
S nakes of black wriggle across the sky
T hrashing flames shooting everywhere
O ceans of rain flood the streets
R oars and rumbles like wild beasts
M onstrous clouds rent the Earth.

Alana Dunion (9)
St Michael's Primary School, Moodiesburn

Autumn Is . . .

Autumn is when it gets colder
Autumn is Hallowe'en
Autumn is when squirrels gather nuts for winter
Autumn is when conkers are brown and shiny
Autumn is when animals hibernate
Autumn is when fireworks go off in the sky.

Brendan Johnson (7)
St Michael's Primary School, Moodiesburn

Autumn Is . . .

Autumn is when days get darker
Autumn is when night comes early
Autumn is when animals hibernate
Autumn is when wasps and bees die
Autumn is crunchy leaves
Autumn is excellent.

Rachel Cannon (7)
St Michael's Primary School, Moodiesburn

Thunderstorm

(Inspired by 'Waterfall' by Cynthia Rider)

T hunderstorm, thunderstorm go away, come on back another night
H ailstones, rain and gale force winds, what a terrible sight
U nder the covers in your bedroom, scared to death in horror
N ervously scared, you're frightened to move
D rains fill up with water and flood streets and towns
E ver so frightful, you'd want to scream
R oaring winds that blow houses down
S trikes of lightning come from nowhere
T hunderclouds rend the earth
O verhead are stars above that the light fades
R eflecting light from lightning that strikes every minute
M orning arrives, the light shines bright, not another storm in sight.

Ashley Welch (8)
St Michael's Primary School, Moodiesburn

Thunderstorm

(Inspired by 'Waterfall' by Cynthia Rider)

T osses in turbulent torrents
H undreds of clouds
U nder the bed I was very still
N obody is out playing
D ads and mums keep their children in
E very day is either raining or miserable
R aining every day
S torm is noisy and storm is dark
T he children are watching TV
O ver the clouds a bird flies
R ainbow is in the sky
M orning has arrived, it is a sunny day.

Joni Moultrie (9)
St Michael's Primary School, Moodiesburn

Thunderstorm

(Inspired by 'Waterfall' by Cynthia Rider)

T ossing and turning as you lie in your bed
H isses and roars as the night goes by
U nder the blankets, nervously scared
N obody out, I freaked out
D amp and dull as the power goes off
E veryone frightened and scared
R attling and roaring are the noises it makes
S nuggled up inside as the night goes on
T ucked up in bed all cosy and sound
O ut of the window you see the light
R aindrops falling down from the sky
M orning arrives, sun is out, thunder is away, let's go out.

Danielle Cochrane (9)
St Michael's Primary School, Moodiesburn

Thunderstorm

(Inspired by 'Waterfall' by Cynthia Rider)

T he moon comes out, the mountain is dark
H itting and slapping, the storm goes on
U p rushes a storm from far away
N o wonder you're told to stay away
D estiny is closing in
E xplosive the storm stays
R attling and rumbling off the ground
S till in the house nice and warm
T he rain is getting heavy and is falling in floods
O bnoxious a storm is
R eflecting off the puddles, does not look very nice
M y imagination stirs.

Colette McGarry (9)
St Michael's Primary School, Moodiesburn

Sadness

Sadness is blue like the stormy seas
It sounds like me in a sad mood crying
It tastes like some tasty fruits
It smells like the dead flowers
It looks like shimmering water
It feels like soft hair
Sadness reminds me of caterpillars.

Katie MacKenzie (9)
St Thomas' Primary School, Neilston

Happiness

Happiness is green like the grass in the countryside
It sounds like wind blowing in the trees
It tastes like big oranges
It smells like fresh air when it's stopped raining
It looks like a waterfall
It feels like wind blowing into your face
Happiness reminds me of when I went to my friend's party.

Megan McCarron (9)
St Thomas' Primary School, Neilston

Sadness

Sadness is red like a fierce exploding volcano.
Sadness sounds like a cremation funeral.
Sadness tastes like tears leaking slowly.
Sadness feels like the worst in the world.
Sadness smells like a blocked up nose.
Sadness looks like the world in pain.
Sadness reminds me of my mum being sad.

Joe Foy (9)
St Thomas' Primary School, Neilston

Sadness

Sadness is red like blood
It sounds like screaming
It tastes like burnt toast
It smells like wet paint
It looks like a fire-hot blade
It feels like a flood
Sadness reminds me of death and blood.

Katelin Wilson (8)
St Thomas' Primary School, Neilston

Love

Love is yellow like the sun above us all.
It sounds like the birds are chirping in the trees.
It tastes like the kiss of a girl.
It smells like a girl's lipstick.
It looks like a sunflower.
It feels like love is in the air.
Love reminds me of kissing.

Jordan Whiteford (9)
St Thomas' Primary School, Neilston

Happiness

Happiness is green like green grass in the countryside.
It sounds like a conker tree.
It tastes like a dark orange on a tree.
It smells like air when you breathe in and out.
It looks like brown worms on the grass.
It feels like mint you get for your dinner.

Sophie McAvoy (9)
St Thomas' Primary School, Neilston

Love

Love is white like a beautiful dove.
It sounds like church bells ringing.
It tastes like love heart chocolate.
It smells like beautiful flowers swaying in the breeze.
It looks like a happy smile on someone's face.
It feels like happiness so great it's unbelievable.
Love reminds me of my mum.

Annelouise McCullagh (9)
St Thomas' Primary School, Neilston

Anger

Anger is red like explosion fires.
It sounds like hot flames down your shirt.
It tastes like hot chillies in your mouth.
It smells like a box of smoke.
It looks like hot blood.
It feels like you are going to explode.
Anger reminds me of hot fire.

Hannah Moore (8)
St Thomas' Primary School, Neilston

Sadness

Sadness is blue like a stormy sea.
It sounds like the cry of a drowning man.
It tastes like clear water.
It smells like rotten fruit.
It looks like sour lemon.
It feels really creepy.
Sadness reminds me of the flames of fires.

Sara Howie (8)
St Thomas' Primary School, Neilston

Anger

Anger is red like an exploding tomato.
It sounds like Hurricane Frances.
It tastes like black water from all over the ground.
It smells like the wind blowing side to side.
It looks like you are in a temper.
It feels like you are so angry.
Anger reminds me of fighting with my friend.

Kendle Keenan (9)
St Thomas' Primary School, Neilston

Anger

Anger is black like the stones on the ground.
It sounds like a hurricane terrorising the town.
It tastes like brown mud on the black ground.
It smells like rotten eggs that are just not right.
It looks like rain that nobody likes.
It feels like grey wind swaying side to side.
Anger reminds me of getting grounded and sent to bed.

Brogan McFlynn (9)
St Thomas' Primary School, Neilston

Anger

Anger is red like an amazing hot fire.
It sounds like thunder breaking through the sky.
It tastes like rotten turnip.
It smells like burning hot fire.
It feels like everyone hates you.
Anger reminds me of falling out.

Daniella Di Bona (9)
St Thomas' Primary School, Neilston

Sadness

Sadness is blue like the blue sky above.
It sounds like thunder and lightning.
It tastes like salty water out of the sea.
It smells like seaweed sitting on the sand.
It looks like stars in the sky.
It feels like icy water.
It reminds me of my boyfriend.

Nicola Finnigan (9)
St Thomas' Primary School, Neilston

Sadness

Sadness is red like a person bleeding to death
It sounds like screaming in the ear
It tastes like blood driving fear into the heart of men
It smells like onions being peeled making me cry
It looks like a dead goldfish floating in its bowl
It feels like a broken heart
Sadness reminds me of a cut knee.

Liam Brady (9)
St Thomas' Primary School, Neilston

Love

Love is yellow like the beautiful sun above.
It sounds like birds singing in the trees.
It tastes like love heart chocolate.
It smells like red roses.
It looks like something wonderful.
It feels like a dove in your arms.
Love reminds me of my family.

Danielle Higgins (8)
St Thomas' Primary School, Neilston

Anger

Anger is red like someone has shot you and blood
                                    is running out of your body.
It sounds like a girl crying for her mum because she is being bullied.
It tastes like a black, rotten, red blood apple.
It smells like someone smoking and the smoke you
                                    breathe in will make you faint.
It looks like your friend has turned into your enemy.
It feels like all you have in your heart is shame, so you fight.
Anger reminds me of when I was going to fight for my family.

Neil Morran (8)
St Thomas' Primary School, Neilston

Happiness

Happiness is green for the meadows in the countryside.
It sounds like birds chirping in the trees.
It tastes like the water from the mountain spring hills in Scotland.
It smells like the air in the lovely blue sky.
It looks like the bright yellow sun in the meadow.
It feels like the spring air.
Happiness reminds me of the sound of music.

Adam Martin (9)
St Thomas' Primary School, Neilston

Happiness

Happiness is gold like the colour of a cup.
It sounds like birds going tweet, tweet, tweet, tweet.
It tastes like fresh fruit from a tree.
It smells like some fresh orange juice.
It looks like the nature beginning again.
Happiness reminds me of my girlfriend.

Adam Forde (8)
St Thomas' Primary School, Neilston

Love

Love is yellow like the beautiful sunshine.
It sounds like birds whistling in the trees.
It tastes like love heart chocolate.
It smells like white roses.
It looks like a sunflower glimmering in the sun.
It feels like happiness running through your body.
Love reminds me of my family.

Gemma Mackie (8)
St Thomas' Primary School, Neilston

Love

Love is yellow like the beautiful sun above.
It sounds like birds singing in the trees.
It tastes like an orange cream.
It smells like the open fresh air.
It looks like a newly grown sunflower.
It feels like the love for two people who were meant to be together.
Love reminds me of world peace.

Matthew Gallanagh (9)
St Thomas' Primary School, Neilston

Sadness

Sadness is grey like a thundercloud passing over the hills.
It sounds like lightning hitting the ground.
It tastes like heavy rain touching my tongue.
It smells like fog all dark and misty.
It feels like a twister destroying the world.
It reminds me of losing my very best friend.

Adam Kilian (9)
St Thomas' Primary School, Neilston

Happiness

Happiness is orange like a beautiful juicy orange
Happiness sounds like cars passing by the window in the morning
Happiness tastes like lovely rum and raisin ice cream
Happiness smells like Mum's cooking at teatime
Happiness feels like getting a kiss from my mum
Happiness reminds me of my bed so hot and comfy.

Craig Doherty (10)
St Thomas' Primary School, Neilston

Love

Love is pink like a flower in the garden
It sounds like the laughing of happiness
It tastes like my best dinner
It smells like the nice fresh air
It feels like you have won the lottery
It reminds me of furry wee puppies.

David John Dunn (10)
St Thomas' Primary School, Neilston

Happiness

Happiness is yellow like a bright sun in the sky
It tastes like my favourite sweets
It sounds like birds cheeping in the wind
It smells like my mum's cooking in the kitchen
It feels like winning the lottery
It reminds me of my family.

Gemma MacAlister (10)
St Thomas' Primary School, Neilston

Sadness

Sadness is the colour grey
It's a dark, depressing room
It sounds like crying in the distance
It is as dry as a bone
Smelling like an old damp rug
It looks like a blank book
It is as if no one wants you
It reminds me of my dead relatives.

Nicky McCarron (11)
St Thomas' Primary School, Neilston

Happiness

Happiness is the colour yellow, like the sunshine.
It sounds like birds tweeting in the trees.
It smells like a buttercup that grows in the meadow.
It tastes like a picnic on the beach.
It looks like the world is the right way round for me.
It feels like the world is perfect.
It reminds me of the good old days.

Cameron Coyne (10)
St Thomas' Primary School, Neilston

Anger

Anger is red like a devil in the flames
It sounds like a dash of thunder
It tastes like burnt toast
It smells like smoke in the distance
It feels like war
It reminds me of a bull charging round the bullring.

Anthony Finnigan (10)
St Thomas' Primary School, Neilston

Happiness

Happiness is yellow like a happy, exciting friendship
It sounds like a bird singing beautifully in your ear
It tastes like a yummy, delicious chocolate bar
It smells like a pretty, freshly picked pansy
It feels like a big hug and kiss from your mum
It reminds me of lots of love and peace.

Martin Gribben
St Thomas' Primary School, Neilston

Happiness

Happiness is yellow like a lovely bright morning
It sounds like the birds singing in the trees
It smells like the beautiful summer breeze
It tastes like my favourite dish
It feels like I am swimming in the sea with the fish
It reminds me of the beautiful summer sun
It reminds me of my great mum!

Rebecca McMullen (10)
St Thomas' Primary School, Neilston

Anger

Anger is red like a fierce, burning fire
It sounds like sizzling sausages
It tastes like burnt toast
It smells like ashes
It feels like a hot iron
It reminds me of a barbecue gone wrong.

Mhairi Hannigan (10)
St Thomas' Primary School, Neilston

Happiness

Happiness is yellow like a hot, beautiful sun.
It sounds like the birds singing in the trees.
It tastes like a lovely bar of chocolate.
It smells like a daffodil.
It feels like I've won a medal.
It reminds me of holiday in Spain.

Christopher Wilson (10)
St Thomas' Primary School, Neilston

Sadness

Sadness is blue like the freezing cold sea.
It sounds like someone upset and crying.
It tastes like raw vegetables.
It smells like the salt water when I'm down at the beach.
It feels like my heart is breaking very slowly.
It reminds me of a sad movie.

Nicola Queen (10)
St Thomas' Primary School, Neilston

Anger

Anger is red like a fierce, scary dragon
It sounds like a wooden house catching fire and spreading instantly
It tastes like the ashes from a big fire
It feels like hot, boiling water in a kettle
It reminds me of a volcano erupting full of boiling hot lava.

Daniel MacRae (10)
St Thomas' Primary School, Neilston

Fear

Fear is blue like waves clashing off the rocks.
It sounds like screams nipping your ear drums.
Fear feels like water being frozen into ice which does not feel nice.
It looks like a dark cloud covering the sky.
It reminds me of a shark looking you in the eye.
Fear tastes like dripping sweat from a worried body
And it smells like smoke surrounding you.

Rebecca Lees (11)
St Thomas' Primary School, Neilston

Happiness

Is happiness the wonders of a rainbow?
Is it the joy of spring?
Is it all of the lambs being born?
Is it a baby having birth?
Is it a smile?
Is it making a new friend?
Is it the night of bonfire?
Happiness can be whatever you desire.

Carrie-Ann Aitken (8)
St Thomas' Primary School, Neilston

Sadness

Sadness is grey like a cloudy, miserable day.
It sounds like a storm coming my way.
It tastes like out of date milk.
It smells like my bin before the cleanout day.
It feels like a hard rock coming to hit me.
It reminds me of crying after a sad movie.

Tessa Jones (10)
St Thomas' Primary School, Neilston

Happiness

Happiness is a bright, cheery yellow
It is like the burning sun in the sky
It sounds like hummingbirds singing their sweet lullaby
It smells like sweet, cheery roses blooming in the summer
It has a great taste, joy running inside me
It looks like a colourful rainbow hovering above me
It feels like fireworks bursting inside me
It reminds me of the cheerful faces all around me.

Christopher Skea (11)
St Thomas' Primary School, Neilston

Love

Love is like the colours of a red heart pounding in your soul
A lovely scent of the pink flowers in the garden
It tastes like sweet chocolate melting in your mouth
It looks like a heart overflowing with love
It's like shining stars twinkling through the night
It reminds me of people in love.

Kayleigh Shaw (11)
St Thomas' Primary School, Neilston

Sadness

Sadness is black like a deep hole in the ground.
It sounds like millions of insects crawling around.
It tastes like bitter, cold dirt and rock.
It smells like something intoxicating.
It feels like a rat sitting on my head.
It reminds me of death and sorrow.

Brian Sinclair (10)
St Thomas' Primary School, Neilston

Sadness

Sadness is grey like a dove all alone
It sounds like a human's cry for help
It tastes like salty tears on my cheeks
It smells like the sewers underneath the city
It feels like a ghost haunting me all day
It reminds me of people crying with nothing else to hear.

Connor McLaughlin (10)
St Thomas' Primary School, Neilston

Anger

Anger is red like a dangerous, terrible, fierce fire-breathing dragon
It sounds like an angry dragon roaring
It tastes like hot, hot fire
It smells like smoke burning
It feels as though a dangerous dragon is going to attack
It reminds me of hot, hot fire and smoke.

Gary Lambie (10)
St Thomas' Primary School, Neilston

Happiness

Happiness is yellow like the pretty daffodils.
It sounds like the fruits falling from the trees.
It tastes like a delicious double chocolate cake.
It smells like the lemon in a jug of tasty juice.
It feels like big happy smiles all around you.
It reminds me of my caring family.

John-Gerard Shepherd (10)
St Thomas' Primary School, Neilston

Sadness

Sadness is blue like the ocean, with its big waves and sea creatures
It sounds like a very gentle wind
It tastes like salt and dirty river water
It smells of salt and the wide open sea
It feels very smooth but with enormous, towering waves
It reminds me of a big, gigantic flood.

Gareth Toner (10)
St Thomas' Primary School, Neilston

Sadness

Sadness is black like undreamable, horrible death!
It sounds like the screams that are horrifying and deadly
It tastes like the most terrible thing ever made
It smells like rotten, disgusting, old left out flesh
The feeling is tingling shivers running up my back
It reminds me of the sadness and pain of people dying.

Jack Heaney (10)
St Thomas' Primary School, Neilston

Happiness

Happiness is yellow like a big juicy banana.
It sounds like the birds chirping in the sky.
It tastes like a lovely sweet pineapple.
It smells like a lovely, beautiful perfume.
It feels like winning a trophy.
It reminds me of the lovely daffodils growing in my garden.

Jordan Allan (9)
St Thomas' Primary School, Neilston

Fear

Fear is the colour of black, a depressing colour.
Fear sounds like a baby screaming.
It smells of a black house burning.
It tastes of a tingle on your tongue.
It looks like someone has been petrified.
It feels as if your heart has stopped.
Somehow it reminds me of the war in Iraq
Because war is depressing and fearful
And one day that could be us.

Liam Morran (10)
St Thomas' Primary School, Neilston

Sadness

Sadness is blue like the windiest sea.
It sounds like the howl of a whale.
It tastes like a horrible kind of poison.
It smells like the blood of a victim.
It looks like the worst storm.
It feels like your heart stopping.
Sadness reminds me of my great grandpa.

Aidan Reid (8)
St Thomas' Primary School, Neilston

Happiness

Happiness is yellow like a buttercup.
It sounds like the birds chirping in the sky.
It tastes like beautiful food on my plate.
It smells like the daffodils that grow in my garden.
It feels like having the best car in the world.
It reminds me of my loving, caring family.

Ryan Higgins (10)
St Thomas' Primary School, Neilston

Happiness

Happiness is ever so bright
It is multicoloured every day and night.
It sounds like a lullaby playing at night
It smells like a lovely red rose standing in the light.
It tastes like chocolate from a friend
Who helps you if you are sad or down.
It looks like a lullaby bird singing through the night.
It feels like a generous deed you have done for the poor
And it reminds me of a meadow filled with sweet, colourful flowers.

Jamie Carmichael (10)
St Thomas' Primary School, Neilston

Love

Love is pink like roses and tulips,
It tastes like chocolate melting in my mouth.
It looks like children playing happily together,
It smells like flowers planted in the meadow.
Love feels like my heart, beating faster and faster,
It reminds me of kindness, happiness and joy
Because love is a wonderful thing.

Jennifer Bell (11)
St Thomas' Primary School, Neilston

Happiness

Happiness is blue like the colour of the sky.
It sounds like a sweet bird singing in the sky.
It looks like children playing with glee.
It feels all warm and happy inside me.
It tastes like ice cream melting on my tongue
And it reminds me of all the happy times
I've had in my life.

Emma Hughes (11)
St Thomas' Primary School, Neilston

Hate

Hate is the smell of smoke
from the raging flames of Hell.
Black! Black! All I can see
when I close my eyes to sleep.
I hear the sounds of screaming,
screeching, squealing as I shout
I hate you!
I taste blood dripping down my chin
every time I speak.
I feel hate,
I can't get this hate out of me.
It looks like gravestones, lightning bolts
and dead bodies.
It reminds me of bullies ganging up
on younger ones.
I hate that!

Jordann Connaghan (11)
St Thomas' Primary School, Neilston

Happiness

Happiness is like a crowd of daffodils
standing in a brightly coloured meadow,
dazzling and dancing, daintily
in the beautiful, bursting, bright yellow sun.
It sounds like a host of angels singing in harmony,
smelling like the petals of a freshly picked rose.
It tastes like the sweetest honey
that has been made by fairies.
It feels like walking across the finest grains
of golden sand spread across a golden beach.
It reminds me of two parents, husband and wife
overflowing with joy as they hold their baby
for the first time in their life.

Amy Smith (10)
St Thomas' Primary School, Neilston

Fear

Fear is like the colour of blue
Like icicles hanging from a roof.
It sounds like a cold wind swaying to and fro
It smells like a peat smell from a coal fire.
It tastes like a sour sweet fizzing on my tongue
It looks like a worrying person being depressed.
It feels like a shiver running down my back
It reminds me of my fear of heights and cows.

Claire Walker (11)
St Thomas' Primary School, Neilston

Happiness

Happiness is the colour of orange
Like beautiful flowers sitting at the edge of the waterfall.
It sounds like the flowing of the water in the river
It smells of burning candles in the night.
Happiness looks like the sun way above the clouds
It tastes of the ice cream that melts in my mouth.
It feels like a flow of fresh air through my body
It reminds me of happy days and having lots of fun.

Amy Bell (11)
St Thomas' Primary School, Neilston

Love

Love is red like the roses in the field
It sounds like the sweet songs of the birds in the trees
It smells like the perfumed air of the morn
And its taste is like the love for a new baby just born.
It looks like kind, caring families who gather
And it feels like your body filling up with emotion
It reminds me of deep feelings and devotion.

Emmy Bradley (10)
St Thomas' Primary School, Neilston

Love

Love is pale blue like a sweet singing blue bird,
It sounds like a peaceful quietness
Where nothing has ever stirred.
It smells like the winter hatching into spring,
It tastes like sugar, a wonderful thing.
It looks like a relaxing sunset,
It feels like a new life that has not started yet.
Reminds me of a soft, sweet song,
That the angel sings all along.

Marianne Gallanagh (11)
St Thomas' Primary School, Neilston

Fear

Fear is black like the dark night sky
It sounds like a bloodthirsty wolf howling right through the night
It smells like flames from the pits of Hell
It tastes like fire burning in my mouth
It looks like an old, creepy house
It feels like someone has a gun to your head
It reminds me of an agonising death.

Stuart Gough (10)
St Thomas' Primary School, Neilston

Love

Love is the colour of a bunch of red and pink roses
Laying on the green grass.
It sounds like birds singing in the warm sun
And smells like melted chocolate.
It tastes like sweet apples and looks like nature.
It feels scary at first but is fine at the end.
Love reminds me of young couples in love.

Lauren Martin (11)
St Thomas' Primary School, Neilston

Sadness

Sadness is dark blue like tears from your eyes,
It sounds like all the rain falling from the skies.
It smells like sour water absorbed by a sponge,
It tastes like the sea, all salty on my tongue.
It looks all damp and dark all around,
It feels like I've been in the blues all year round.
It reminds me of frowns which are smiles upside down,
Sadness is horrible, so stay happy and don't let yourself down.

Michael Aitken (11)
St Thomas' Primary School, Neilston

Love

Love is pink like a small girl's room
It looks like a rose getting ready to bloom
It sounds really quiet like when you go to mass
It looks like growing, golden, green grass
It feels all good and tingly inside
It smells like the air when birds are in the sky
It tastes like chocolate.
May true love never die.

Jack Mayberry (11)
St Thomas' Primary School, Neilston

Hunger

When you are hungry
your tummy really hurts
your insides are dark, dusty.
That horrid wind is screeching
the cat inside is howling and spitting
there's storms in your stomach,
thunder, lightning, earthquakes and hurricanes.

Flossie Taylor (8)
Sandness Primary School, Shetland Islands

Hunger

Hunger is a raging sea,
a howling wind,
or torrential rain.
It's a kite playing
hide-and-seek,
doing loop-the-loop.
Hunger is air in a bottle,
or a trapped fly in a web.
It is a haunted house,
all dark and empty.
Hunger is a chameleon,
always changing colours.
Hunger is a ticking clock,
a jungle drum,
always beating, always beating.

Stuart Macleod (11)
Sandness Primary School, Shetland Islands

Hunger

Hunger is an empty stomach
A sack of bones
A raging wind.
Hunger is a sad stomach
A fly in an empty web
An hallucination of food.
Hunger is a shrivelled prune
A rough sea
A cat scratching in my belly.
Tummy hurts
Feel sick
I could eat an elephant
Dying of hunger.

Miriam Veenhuizen (8)
Sandness Primary School, Shetland Islands

Hunger

Hunger is like a storm
It will never stop blowing
You feel angry and upset
You feel sick and ill.
Hunger is addictive
Grey clouds forming in your head
The world feels dark, empty
Inside yourself feels dark and empty.
Hunger is a dark corner in a room
Like dust on the floor,
Waiting for a bus.
Hunger is like tapped air in a balloon
Like a bare tree in autumn,
Like an unused book,
Like a dead plant,
Like a ticking clock
Waiting until you can eat again.

Daisy Taylor (11)
Sandness Primary School, Shetland Islands

Hunger

You get sad,
Your tummy hurts.
Hunger is bad
Like a ticking clock.
You feel sleepy
Like a fly in an empty web.
It makes you want to
Eat an elephant.

Kieran Wilbourne (8)
Sandness Primary School, Shetland Islands

Hunger

Hunger is a shrivelled prune,
a sack of bones,
an empty bottle.

Hunger is a motorbike,
a rolling ball, a rumbling rock,
going across your belly.

Hunger is like my ears,
goes in one
and out the other.

Hunger plays hide-and-seek,
food hides,
hunger seeks.

Laura Kater (11)
Sandness Primary School, Shetland Islands

Hunger

Hunger is like a howling wind trapped in a bottle
With a kite flying outside making it jealous.
Hunger is a raging sea going around in circles
Being chased by a bag of bones.
It is like a fly caught in a web
Trying to get out.

Callum Sinclair (10)
Sandness Primary School, Shetland Islands

Eight Syllables

Jonathan Livingston Seagull
Trying to be like an eagle
Diving from the skies so high up
While the other birds are sleeping,
Meanwhile antelopes are leaping.

Jonathan Smith
Sgoil Nan Loch, Isle of Lewis

World War Two

W orrying, weary soldiers
O range blazing fire
R elieved my husband's not dead.
L onely men going to war
D oing all they can.

W ar is here, death is here,
A nger through all the village,
R attling, rumbling bombs blowing.

T he air-raid siren going
W omen scared at home.
O h, let the war be stopped.

Charlotte Rowe (10)
Sgoil Nan Loch, Isle of Lewis

World War Two Poem

P eople yelling, helpless cries,
E xplosions everywhere,
A ir-raid sirens, wardens whistle,
R ugers are firing
L exburgh rifles are shooting.

H urt soldiers lying dead and injured,
A ck-acks shooting, planes in flames,
R ed blood everywhere!
B ang! Go the gunshots in the town,
O ur war is over and won,
U nited we stand in celebration
R elief for some loved ones, other families still left home alone.

Shirley MacLeod (11)
Sgoil Nan Loch, Isle of Lewis

Night-Time Fears

In the night when darkness falls,
When all the lights are dim,
Jet-black cats and china dolls
Their shadows tall and thin.
These are my night-time fears.

Howling winds and whispering,
A creak on the stairs,
A sound of something rustling
And so starts the nightmares.
These are my night-time fears.

I hear a bang outside my door,
I see the wardrobe open,
Something's just fallen on the floor,
A toy has just been broken.
These are my night-time fears.

Classes 5B, 6 & 7
Sgoil Nan Loch, Isle of Lewis

World War Two

The red blood spilling across the road
People are crying;
Air attacks coming from everywhere.
The bronze of a bullet going through the air;
People shouting from everywhere.
Young men pretending not to be scared;
Explosions bursting.
Flames . . . houses burning, people in pain;
A man with a bullet in his leg
Resting on a hospital bed.

Ben Duke (11)
Sgoil Nan Loch, Isle of Lewis

When The Snow Falls

When the snow falls
Lumps form, grass hidden.

When the snow falls
Nice crispy, water ridden.

When the snow falls
Kids come, make footprints.

When the snow falls
It melts, no hints.

When the snow falls
Build snowmen, have snowball fights.

When the snow falls
Joy to the world!
We have Christmas lights.

Joshua Coghill (9)
Sgoil Nan Loch, Isle of Lewis

Shh! Listen!

Shh! Listen! What can you hear?
A tiger roaring with pain.

Shh! Listen! What can you hear?
A tiny mouse squeaking aloud.

Shh! Listen! What can you hear?
A monkey swinging from tree to tree.

Shh! What can you hear?
A panda eating bamboo.

Shh! What can you hear?
Animals crying.

Mairi Maclean (9)
Sgoil Nan Loch, Isle of Lewis

War

Worry and fear inside hearts.
Pain in everyone.
Sadness: tears filling.
A bomb makes the world go dark.
People dying: misery happens.
Red and orange fire blazing.

Tia Moore (9)
Sgoil Nan Loch, Isle of Lewis

Cheetah

Fierce,
Violent,
Wild
Cheetah.
Sprinting across the Savannah,
Swiftly,
Powerfully,
Like a speedboat racing across the water.
I would be upset if you disappeared
Cheetah,
Powerful cheetah.

Allana Bell (8)
Shapinsay School, Orkney

Fun

Fun is yellow like a banana.
It tastes like pink candyfloss at the fair.
It looks like a happy and smiley face.
It sounds like laughter going down a slide.
It smells like fresh air when I'm playing with my friends.
It feels like a bouncy castle.

Jake Houston (7)
Shapinsay School, Orkney

Crisp Flavours

Slugs and spiders,
Pepper and petrol,
Chocolate and chilli,
Ink and ivy,
Corn and crabs' legs,
Wax crayons and witches' wigs,
Blood and bogeys,
Grass and green beans,
Jelly and jam,
Hearts and ham.

Steven Leslie (8)
Shapinsay School, Orkney

Wild Cat

Wild
Fluffy
Vicious
Wild cat
Sprinting to the river
Quickly
Mightily
Like a soft rug
I would be real sad if you died
Wild cat,
Fluffy wild cat.

Dan Miller (8)
Shapinsay School, Orkney

Horse

Large
Brown
Adventurous
Horse
Galloping free across fields
Powerfully
Boldly
You are like something mysterious
Galloping on the high hills at sunset
I hope you will be free forever
Horse, adventurous horse.

Gail Zawadski (8)
Shapinsay School, Orkney

Snake

Lengthy
Savage
Poisonous
Snake
Slithering in the grass
Swiftly
Silently
Smooth like a glass bottle
I like the way you coil up
Snake,
Lengthy snake.

Andrew Marwick (8)
Shapinsay School, Orkney

Tiger

Furry
Beastly
Wild
Tiger
Darting across the Savannah
Quickly
Viciously
Like a fur coat
I would be sad if you became extinct
Tiger,
Furry.

Savannah Gorham-Wootton (9)
Shapinsay School, Orkney

Dolphin

Swift
Gentle
Silky
Dolphin leaping into the sky
Powerfully
Mightily
Like a speedboat soaring through the waves
Don't stop moving, don't die
Dolphin,
Gentle dolphin.

Emily Farquharson (10)
Shapinsay School, Orkney

Love

Love is like a big heart, full of romance.
It tastes like a box of delicious chocolates.
It smells like a luscious rose in the garden.
It feels like a fluffy, warm rabbit.
It looks like a grassy hill with flowers on the top
On a sunny day.
It sounds like doves' wings flapping up high.

Rachel Muir (8)
Shapinsay School, Orkney

Happiness

Happiness is pink like a rose.
It smells like the best perfume.
It feels like velvet and cats' fur.
It tastes like strawberries with cream.
It looks like twinkling stars.
It sounds like laughter.

Emma Le-Mar (8)
Shapinsay School, Orkney

The Horse

I woke one cold and soggy morn,
To see deep hills in front of me;
Not the yell of my master or the noise of the farm.

I remember my escape through the dark last night.
Oh to be free is blissful,
I feel so free as I shake my mane and cry out to the air.

I galloped o'er the grassy fields to the lake,
Where I took the first sip as spring bloomed again.

Lisa Hanghoj (10)
South Park Primary School, East Kilbride

My Uncle

He is like a blue, smooth couch
And a funky cruising car.
He is a brave, hissing cat
Or maybe a mystic hat.
I often think he's from space
When I look at his face.
He is like a blooming flowers
Out from a morning shower.
He is a cheery, colourful butterfly
Fluttering high in the sky.

Kayleigh Keddie (11)
Tanshall Primary School, Glenrothes

Mysterious Beast

The giant bamboo eater,
You wouldn't want to meet her,
The teddy of the jungle,
Looks quite soft and harmless but really it can bend a pan
Not to mention kill a man.
Black and white, is quite fat, reminds me of my dusty house mat.
Eyes black same as her back,
She comes from China like my aunt Mima.
Her skin is thick like a very large stick.

Jack King (10)
Tanshall Primary School, Glenrothes

My Dad

He is like a creaky old-fashioned chair,
He's a big, woolly bear.
When he's at work he's like clockwork
And at home he sleeps in his chair.
He sneezes like a horse
And he's like a dark cloud in the morning.

Peter Morton (11)
Tanshall Primary School, Glenrothes

My Budgie

He sleeps
He eats
He tweets.
He really likes to play
Every single day.
He's blue and white
Such a delight.
He flies about my room
Like a witch on a broom.
He blasts off like a zoom!
He's got a lovely orange beak,
But a really noisy squeak.
He stands on his stem
And sleeps like a gem.

Leah Parrott (11)
Tanshall Primary School, Glenrothes

The Scary Black Cat

I have four legs
and two eyes.
I have pointy ears
and a long, curly tail.
I have four paws
and really sharp claws.
Can you guess
what I am?
Here's a clue
I am the enemy
of a dog . . .
miaow.

Daryll Watson (10)
Tanshall Primary School, Glenrothes

My Mum

She's like a comfy cushion
and an open book.
She has a roar of a lion
and is as bright as a parrot.
She is as jolly as a summer's morning
and as beautiful as a sunset on a beach.
Her voice is like the sound of a calm sea
and as clear as a clear sky.
In the morning she is bright as a light
and in the night she is as calm as a calm starlit sky.

Anthony Quinn (11)
Tanshall Primary School, Glenrothes

My Mum

A chair always free to sit on,
A bouncy, happy bed,
A quiet, caring dog,
An always awake cockerel,
The large soul of Britain,
Sounds like the calm beach,
A sparkling morning person ready for the day ahead,
A soldier marching into war.

Alan Chung (9)
Tanshall Primary School, Glenrothes

My Gran

My gran is like a bouncy, big bed,
She shouts like a lion,
Walking to the beach,
Talking all the day,
Out every night,
Sounds like a dog barking all day,
Barking every morning.

John Neil (11)
Tanshall Primary School, Glenrothes

The Fearsome Raptors

The fearsome, prehistoric raptors hunt together for prey
as their young run beside them and play
some violent games.
They run together and get ready with their huge, sharp claws
like a lion does in the present day
but raptors have no paws,
They leap and bound upon the ground
with their huge, strong feet.
their sharp, bloody teeth seem to curl into a smile
as a stegosaurus herd comes into view.
They race to their prey
and the prey runs away
but the young start to fall behind.
The raptors pounce on the juicy young prey
as cats do to mice in the present day.
They rip and they tear
and the sight was a scare,
their green scales turned to red.
This hunt was a
successful one
but I would much
rather eat a burger
in a bun.

Callum Howe (10)
Tanshall Primary School, Glenrothes

My Grandad

He's like an old wooden seat,
like an elephant or rhino with big feet.
On a plane in the rain
or in a churchyard in sunny Spain.
On the windy ocean
in the morning sky
any place, any time.
He'd never commit a silly crime.

Kevin Scott (11)
Tanshall Primary School, Glenrothes

My Dog

She jumps on my bed at night
I always get a huge big fright
My dog Sophie is fun
I always take her out for a run
She barks when she sees another dog at the park
She barks *woof, woof,* when she's hungry
She goes for a sleep after a walk
Then I go out and play with chalk
She smells her tea.
She's *fun.*

Gillian Allison (10)
Tanshall Primary School, Glenrothes

My Ultimate Best Mom

As clean as a see-through, shiny glass table,
She has an open window for me,
Her laughter is like a funny hyena,
A rooster who jumps out of bed,
She is as fast as a gazelle at work,
A sound of birds singing that makes me happy,
The sound of a hissing snake ready to come and get me,
An owl that hoots in the night.

Demi Leung (10)
Tanshall Primary School, Glenrothes

My Mum

A calm and beautiful rocking chair swinging in the breeze,
A bunny rabbit bouncing around in the sunshine,
Rush hour at a busy train station and a fast and furious hoover
running around the house,
The sound of a roaring lion and a newborn kitten,
Dressed up to the nines
On a perfect day.

Ross Cooper (11)
Tanshall Primary School, Glenrothes

My Mad Cousin

She's a bouncy, inflatable chair,
She's a bright, sparkling table,
She's a berserk, scratching cat,
A crazy, kicking kangaroo.
A beautiful, amazing poppy field,
She's a drizzling waterfall.
A dripping tap,
She's the sound of *thunder!*
She's the pitch-black night,
The light day,
Of course she's my cousin.

Riah Holmes (10)
Tanshall Primary School, Glenrothes

My Gran

A very peaceful chair in the corner,
A very sleepy bed,
As quiet as a tiger,
As drowsy as a cat,
In her big old tired house,
A microscopic garden,
A tiny sigh,
A mighty yawn
All night long.

Conner Webster (11)
Tanshall Primary School, Glenrothes

My Friend

He's a bouncy bed and a soft, cuddly pillow,
He's a little boy who is always having fun,
He's a waterfall that's always running,
He sounds like a little mouse and a scary bear when he is angry,
He is a picnic in the summer's afternoon.

Kyle Young (11)
Tanshall Primary School, Glenrothes

Koala Bear

I am a tiny, cute animal,
Bear-like and climbs trees.
I am black and white,
and come out at night
And sometimes I might
give you a fright.
I sometimes pop my claws out,
I scratch, scrape and peel what I eat,.
When I scream it's really loud,
and when you hold me,
I cling onto you.

Sabah Fiaz (10)
Tanshall Primary School, Glenrothes

My Grandad M

He's a laptop on legs
He's as comfy as a chair
He eats like a pig
He's as tough as a horse
And as fit as a fiddle
His voice is like a bell
And he's like the sunshine
In the morning.

Stephen Foley (11)
Tanshall Primary School, Glenrothes

The Dolphin

I love to swim,
I make a funny noise and smile,
I'm always jumping and going through rings and hoops,
I like to entertain people,
You can see me at shows
And I have a pair of flippers.

Debra Runatsa (10)
Tanshall Primary School, Glenrothes

My Cockatiel - Haiku

Special little bird
Yellow, orange, white and black
Chirping so sweetly.

Sophie Tulloch
Tingwall Primary School, Shetland Islands

The Wee Orange Fishy - Haiku

Wee orange fishy
Went on a big flat dishy
Gobbled up quickly.

Danny Garrick (10)
Tingwall Primary School, Shetland Islands

Cats - Haiku

Cats are small and cute
They can purr all day and night
Cats can sleep all day.

Bruce Johnstone (10)
Tingwall Primary School, Shetland Islands

Sun - Haiku

The sun is shining
Let's all go outside and play
Soon it will be gone!

Jonny Sinclair (10)
Tingwall Primary School, Shetland Islands

Cheetah - Haiku

Speedy cheetah runs
Into an enormous tree
Oh, watch out speedy!

Lee Graham (9)
Tingwall Primary School, Shetland Islands

Sunshine - Haiku

Sunshine through the trees
Making patterns on the ground
On a lovely day.

Tom Sclater (10)
Tingwall Primary School, Shetland Islands

The Venus Flytrap - Haiku

Catching all the flies,
In the blinking of your eyes
Flies, flies, flies, flies, flies.

Jenni Leask (10)
Tingwall Primary School, Shetland Islands

Flowers - Haiku

A flower's petals
Bees taking nectar away
On a summer's day.

Emma Johnson (9)
Tingwall Primary School, Shetland Islands

Snowman - Haiku

Snowman getting big
Snowflakes are coming low, down low
Time for snow to go.

Rhanna Dawson (9)
Tingwall Primary School, Shetland Islands

Rain - Haiku

Rain falls on the ground
Making puddles everywhere
Children splish, splash, splosh!

Matthew Irvine (9)
Tingwall Primary School, Shetland Islands

Cats - Haiku

Cats are nice because
Cats are so good at catching mice
Hear them miaow and purr.

Sarah Hunter (10)
Tingwall Primary School, Shetland Islands

Eddy - Haiku

Eddy is my cat
He has sharp claws to catch mice
He doesn't like rats.

Jack Hardie (10)
Tingwall Primary School, Shetland Islands